GRADE 4

Review, Practice, & Mastery of

COMMON CORE
ENGLISH LANGUAGE ARTS
STATE STANDARDS

Reviewers:

Amy Barr • Park Hill School District • Park Hi...
Tracie Baumgartner • Valley View School Dis... • Bolingbrook, IL
Barbara Burns • Lammersville Unified School District • Mountain House, CA
Karen Cooke • Cobb County School District • Marietta, GA
Amy Corr • Douglas County School District • Highlands Ranch, CO
Rachel Nichols • Lower Merion School District • Ardmore, PA
Arlene Peters • Orange County Public Schools • Orlando, FL
Brian Selling • Community Day Charter School • Lawrence, MA
Kim Sheehy • Sauquoit Valley Central Schools • Sauquoit, NY
Beverly Smith • Corona-Norco Unified School District • Ontario, CA
Colleen Thomas • Sandwich Public Schools • Sandwich, MA
Holly Walker • Whitman-Hanson Regional School District • Hanson, MA

© 2013 **Perfection Learning**®
www.perfectionlearning.com

8 9 10 11 12 PP 18 17 16 15 14

35332
ISBN-13: 978-0-7891-8228-9

Printed in the United States of America

To the Student

This book will help you review, practice, and master the English Language Arts Common Core State Standards for Grade 4. Here are the steps to follow to use this book.

1. Take the Tryout Test over Reading Literature, Reading Informational Text, and Language and check your answers. Use the chart at the bottom of this page to find out your strengths and weaknesses in the areas covered. Remember the questions that are hard for you to answer. They will be the types of questions you need to work on the most.

2. Work through the units that follow the Tryout Test. The lessons in each unit review example items and provide a practice test based on the standards. Fill in the Keeping Score chart on page 155 as you complete each practice test.

3. After completing all the lessons, take the Mastery Test. Your score on this test will show your understanding of the Common Core standards.

4. Work through the writing workshops section of this book. These lessons will help you learn how to read a writing prompt and how to get your ideas down on paper in a clear, organized manner.

Reading Literature	Tryout Test Items	Mastery Test Items
Unit One—Key Ideas and Details		
Lesson 1 Explain and Infer	7	5, 9
Lesson 2 Character, Setting, and Plot	9, 12	3, 18
Lesson 3 Theme and Summary	6, 15	4, 7
Unit Two—Craft and Structure		
Lesson 4 Word Choice	1, 11, 14	1, 6, 14
Lesson 5 Poetry	3, 4	12, 13, 15
Lesson 6 Drama	8	10, 11
Unit Three—Integration of Knowledge and Ideas		
Lesson 7 Point of View and Illustrations	2, 5	2, 8, 16
Lesson 8 Comparing and Contrasting Stories	18	20
Reading Informational Text	**Tryout Test Items**	**Mastery Test Items**
Unit Four—Key Ideas and Details		
Lesson 9 Explain and Infer	19, 30	36, 37
Lesson 10 Main Ideas and Supporting Details	21, 27, 29	29, 32, 33, 35
Unit Five—Craft and Structure		
Lesson 11 Text Structures	20, 23, 24, 25, 26	21, 22, 28
Lesson 12 Reasons and Evidence	28	30, 31
Unit Six—Integration of Knowledge and Ideas		
Lesson 13 Text Features	22, 33	23, 24
Lesson 14 Comparing and Contrasting Texts	34, 35	38, 39, 40
Language	**Tryout Test Items**	**Mastery Test Items**
Unit Seven—Standard English		
Lesson 15 Grammar	41, 42, 45	50, 51
Lesson 16 Usage	43, 49	46, 47, 49
Lesson 17 Phrases and Sentences	40, 50, 51	52, 53, 54
Unit Eight—Capitalization, Punctuation, and Spelling		
Lesson 18 Capitalization and Spelling	36, 37, 38, 39, 44	41, 43, 44, 45
Lesson 19 Punctuation	46, 47, 48	42, 48
Unit Nine—Vocabulary		
Lesson 20 Word Meanings	10, 16, 31, 32	17, 25, 34
Lesson 21 Word Parts and Relationships	13, 17	19, 26, 27

Common Core Grade 4

Table of Contents

continued

Reading Informational Text

Language

Unit Eight—Capitalization, Punctuation, and Spelling

Unit Nine—Vocabulary

Writing

Standards Key: RL.4 = Reading Literature, Grade 4 Standard; RI.4 = Reading Informational Text, Grade 4 Standard; RL.4 = Language, Grade 4 Standard; W.4 = Writing, Grade 4 Standard.

Note: A complete correlation of Common Core State Standards can be found in the Grade 4 Teacher Guide.

Tryout Test: Part 1
Estimated time: 30 minutes

Directions: Read the passage. Then answer the questions that follow.

Mean Mary

1 “I *love* your shirt,” said Mean Mary one day
2 as she rolled her eyes and then walked away.
3 I waited until she was long gone,
4 Then I looked down to see what I had on.
5 I didn't think it was as bad as she had made it sound;
6 It's hard to be fashionable with hand-me-downs.
7 But I don't complain because I know my mom tries.
8 She works two jobs and never so much as sighs.
9 I took a deep breath, then ran to catch the bus.
10 I didn't think Mary was worth raising a fuss.
11 When Mom got home from work that night,
12 She asked me if I knew a girl named Mary Wright.
13 I thought of the girl and the comments she made,
14 The meanest girl in the whole fourth grade.
15 “Poor girl,” Mom said, “I work with her dad.
16 The whole situation is very sad.”
17 “Her mom passed away earlier this year,
18 And now her brother's sick too, they fear.”
19 The next day at school, I knew what I had to do.
20 I found Mary bent down, tying her shoe.
21 She stood and she glared—if looks could kill!
22 But I swallowed hard and mustered up all my will.
23 When she snarled, “Why don't you get lost for a while!”
24 I remembered she needed a friend—so I smiled.

1 The author uses the phrase <u>rolled her eyes</u> in line 2 to show that Mary—

A liked the shirt very much.

B saw something on the ceiling.

C didn't really like the shirt.

D had poor eyesight.

2 The illustration included with this poem helps readers—

   A understand why Mean Mary is so mean.

   B learn about bullies.

   C imagine what Mean Mary's life is like.

   D imagine what Mean Mary might look like.

3 This passage is—

   A prose because it rhymes.

   B poetry because it rhymes.

   C drama because it has characters and dialogue.

   D drama because it tells a story.

4 Which lines explain why Mary needs a friend?

   A lines 4–7

   B lines 11–12

   C lines 15–18

   D lines 22–24

5 Who is telling the story? Is the story in first-person or third-person point of view? Support your answer with details from the text. (3 points)

_____

_____

_____

_____

_____

_____

_____

6 Which of the following sayings BEST explains the theme of the story?

    A Don't get mad, get even.

    B Don't judge a person until you understand his or her situation.

    C Beauty is only skin deep.

    D If you can't say anything nice, don't say anything at all.

7 From the poem, we can infer that Mary—

    A doesn't have any family.

    B is the only mean girl in the fourth grade.

    C is mean because of the hard things in her life.

    D will be nice to the person telling the story.

Directions: Read the passage. Then answer the questions that follow.

from Almost Sisters

ACT I, Scene 2

It is an early spring evening in Gettysburg, Pennsylvania, during the American Civil War. SALLIE RANDALL sits across the kitchen table from MA.

MA: What do you think, Sallie?

  (SALLIE *stares at her mother with a look of disbelief.*)

MA: It seems your dear pa—may he rest in peace—had a lot of debt. He gave many supplies to the army. I'm not upset; this war is a good cause. But now that he's gone, well, we are as poor as church mice. There is just no other solution.

SALLIE: We could live with Aunt Clara and Uncle Will.

MA: Yes, we could. But I do not want to stay in Gettysburg. There are just too many memories of that <u>horrible</u> battle. Besides, I want us to make a new start together—you and me, Sallie.

SALLIE: But what about my friends and Aunt Clara and Uncle Will?

MA: We'll meet new people, make new friends. You know we will. I sold the store to pay off our debt and have a small sum left to start our new life. I've been reading about the Homestead Act. It says that 160 acres of land is available to the head of any household. (MA *sits up straight and points to herself.*) That's me. If we live there for five years and improve the land, it will be ours, for free. We can raise crops and animals, Sallie. We can provide for ourselves.

SALLIE: But Ma! We don't know how to farm!

MA: That is why I have arranged to work at a neighbor's farm in Kansas. His wife passed away; he is a widower with a son and daughter around your age. I will keep house for them and he will teach us how to work our land. Our land, Sallie. (MA *reaches across the table to take* SALLIE's *hands. She speaks softly now.*) Can I count on you? Shall we step out in faith and start a new life together?

SALLIE: (*Thinks for a few moments, then smiles.*) Yes, Ma. You can count on me.

8   Describe the setting of the play. Refer to specific parts of the play in your answer. (3 points)

_____

_____

_____

_____

_____

9   What BEST helps you understand that Ma feels proud to be the head of the household?

  A Ma's line: *But I do not want to stay in Gettysburg.*
  B Sallie's line: *But Ma! We don't know how to farm!*
  C The stage direction: MA *sits up straight and points to herself.*
  D Ma's line: *He is a widower with a son and daughter around your age.*

10 Reread this sentence from the selection.

There are just too many memories of that <u>horrible</u> battle.

Which synonym is the BEST replacement for <u>horrible</u> as it is used in the selection?

  A evil
  B frightful
  C monstrous
  D awful

11 Based upon context clues, the phrase *as poor as church mice* means Ma and Sallie—

    A go to church a lot.

    B have no money.

    C are very quiet.

    D have no faith.

Directions: Read the passage. Then answer the questions that follow.

The Raven and the Star Fruit Tree

Long ago, two brothers lived in a village in the country of Vietnam. When their father died, they inherited his large fortune.

The older brother took almost the entire fortune for himself, leaving his younger brother with only a tiny part of their father's land. On the land grew a single star fruit tree. The younger brother, who respected and loved his older brother, tried to make the best of the situation. He and his wife carefully watered the tree every day. They planned to make a living by selling the tree's fruit.

But when the fruit ripened and was ready to pick, a giant raven flew toward the younger brother's house. It landed on the tree and began to eat the star fruit. Every day the raven came and ate more of the fruit. The younger brother grew very worried. He decided to speak to the raven.

"Please, raven," he said. "If you eat all the star fruit, I cannot make a living. My wife and children will go hungry."

"Do not worry," answered the raven. "I will repay you with gold. But first you must make a bag exactly three hands long."

The younger brother could hardly believe the raven's words. But he asked his wife to make a bag exactly three hands long. When it was ready, he waited for the raven to <u>return</u>.

The next day the raven flew back to the star fruit tree. The giant bird told the brother to climb on its back, and together they flew off toward the sea.

When they reached a small island, the raven landed near a cave. The raven told the younger brother to enter the cave and fill his bag with gold. Inside the cave were mounds and mounds of shiny golden nuggets. The younger brother quickly filled his bag. Then he returned to the raven, and together they soared across the sea.

The younger brother and his family now had everything they needed. They were very happy.

"Finally, we can prepare a feast in honor of my father," the younger brother told his wife. "I will invite my older brother and his family."

At first the older brother refused the invitation. He did not think the younger brother could afford a feast worthy of their father. But eventually the younger brother persuaded him to come.

When the older brother and his wife arrived, they were surprised to see a table full of fish, pork, chicken, vegetables, rice, and fruits. They thought the younger brother had become a thief. The younger brother then told them about the star fruit, the raven, and the gold. After they ate, the older brother offered to trade all his wealth for the star fruit tree. The younger brother, who respected and loved his older brother, agreed.

When the raven came again to eat the star fruit, the older brother complained. The raven said he would repay him with gold. He said to prepare a bag exactly three hands long.

The next morning the older brother waited, holding a folded bag. He and his wife had decided to make the bag nine hands long instead of three. The older brother grinned when he thought how clever he was to trick the raven. He sat dreaming of the things he could buy with the extra gold.

Soon the raven arrived to carry the older brother away to the island and the cave. In the cave, the older brother scooped up as much gold as he could. He stuffed not only his large bag, but his pockets too. The raven became impatient as he waited. Finally, the older brother finished, and they began to fly across the sea toward home.

But the raven struggled to stay in the air. "I can barely fly," he told the older brother. "You must drop some of the gold into the sea." The brother only held his bag more tightly.

The raven grew more tired every minute. <u>Soon they were flying so low, the raven could feel the sea tickle his claws.</u> He tried to fly higher. Suddenly, one big wave crashed over the raven. The older brother, still clutching his gold, tumbled into the sea. Free of the heavy burden, the raven flapped his wings and flew off.

The raven returned to tell the younger brother what had happened. The younger brother was sad, but his family lived comfortably for the rest of their days.

12 Based on his actions in the story, how would you describe the older brother?

   A greedy

   B respectful

   C funny

   D honest

13 Based on the meaning of the prefix *re-*, what is the meaning of <u>return</u>?

   A not come

   B come back

   C come more often

   D not be able to come

14 Reread this sentence from the passage.

Soon they were flying so low, the raven could feel the sea tickle his claws.

This sentence has what type of literary device?

   A simile

   B metaphor

   C personification

   D rhyme

GO ON

15 Write a summary of the story. Be sure to include the main idea and most important events. (3 points)

_____

_____

_____

_____

_____

_____

_____

_____

Directions: Read the passage. Then answer the questions that follow.

The Baker's Daughter

1   Long ago in England there was a baker who had twin daughters. Strangely enough, they were as different as night and day. One was cheerful and generous, the other grumpy and selfish.

2   One cold and windy evening, the kind daughter was minding the baker's shop. A poor old woman hobbled in, shivering and clutching her heavy cloak. In a voice as weak as mouse's, she asked for a bit of dough.

3   "Why, of course," said the thoughtful daughter and pulled off a large piece.

4   "Would you mind baking it for me, dear?" the old woman asked.

5   "I'd be happy to," said the girl.

6   The old woman seemed to doze in the corner while the dough baked.

7   Suddenly the girl cried out. "Old woman! Look! The loaf is now twice as large."

8   "Because of your kind heart, so it always shall be," said the woman. Throwing off her tattered cloak, she then revealed her true self—a tall and beautiful fairy. She gently touched the girl with her staff. After that, every kind of dough the girl put into the oven doubled in size.

9   Many evenings later, it was the grumpy daughter's turn to <u>mind</u> the baker's shop. The old woman again hobbled into the shop. Leaning on her staff to catch her breath, she squeaked her request for a bit of dough. The girl hesitated. But since her father had told her to be kind to beggars, she finally agreed.

10   "Would you please bake it in the oven for me?" asked the old woman sweetly.

11   <u>The girl sighed as loudly as the wind blowing outside the shop.</u> "If you insist," she said.

12   The old woman again seemed to drift into sleep while the dough baked. When it was done, the baker's daughter discovered the loaf had doubled in size. "That old woman doesn't deserve this much bread," she thought, and put it aside for herself. Then she broke off another, smaller piece of dough and put it in the oven.

13   But this loaf grew even larger than the first! "The old woman certainly doesn't deserve a loaf as large as this," she thought. And again, the daughter put it aside. Then she dropped into the oven a piece of dough the size of her thumbnail.

14   Lo and behold, this loaf swelled to fill the entire oven! And when the grumpy daughter opened the door, she almost fainted from the delicious smell. Juicy fruit bits and crunchy nuts were bursting through the shiny sugar coating. The daughter very quickly set the huge loaf aside for herself.

15   Soon the old woman woke from her rest and asked, "Is my bread done?"

16   "Hoo-hoo!" laughed the daughter. "I'm afraid it burned up in the oven."

17   "What?" the old woman replied. "I dare you to repeat that!"

18   "Hoo-hoo!" teased the thoughtless girl.

19   "If hoo-hoo is all you can say, then say it for the rest of your days!" The old woman tapped the girl with her staff. The girl <u>instantly</u> became an owl and flew hoo-hooing out into the night.

---

16 Read the dictionary entry for the word <u>mind</u>.

> **mind** *n.* **1.** the part of a body that thinks; the brain
> **2.** a person who thinks *v.* **3.** to look after **4.** to obey

Which definition BEST fits the way <u>mind</u> is used in paragraph 9?

A definition 1

B definition 2

C definition 3

D definition 4

17 The root word of <u>instantly</u> in paragraph 19 is—

A *in.*

B *instant.*

C *ant.*

D *ly.*

Directions: Use both "The Raven and the Star Fruit Tree" and "The Baker's Daughter" to answer the question below.

18   These two stories are from different countries. Yet they both share this message: those who are too greedy will be punished. Explain how both stories show this message. Who is too greedy in each story? How do you know they are greedy? Tell what happens to the greedy person in the end. (5 points)

_____

_____

_____

_____

_____

_____

_____

_____

_____

_____

_____

_____

_____

_____

Take a break. Then go on to Part 2.

Directions: Read the passage. Then answer the questions that follow.

Spring!

Chapter 1

The Vernal Equinox

The first day of spring is called the *vernal equinox*. The word *equinox* means "equal night." On the vernal equinox, day and night are the same length. It happens around March 21 in the Northern Hemisphere and around September 22 in the Southern Hemisphere.

Signs of Spring

As spring gets under way, the days begin to lengthen and the air warms. Soon nature responds. Insects buzz and flowers bloom.

The Earth's surface slowly begins to warm. Water warms more slowly than land. The warming atmosphere causes wind patterns to change. Moisture begins to evaporate from the Earth's surface.

Rainfall

What goes up eventually comes down. When water evaporates, it rises into the atmosphere and forms clouds. Later these clouds will release the water as rain. The amount of water on Earth always stays the same. The only thing that changes is how weather patterns spread it around from season to season and year to year. This is known as the **hydrologic cycle**, or the **water cycle**.

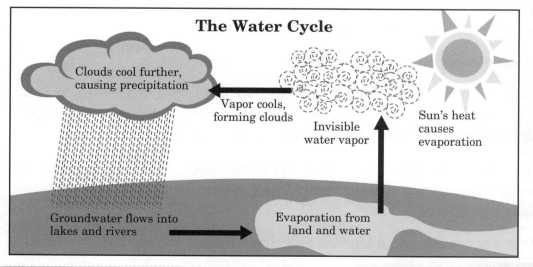

The Water Cycle

Clouds cool further, causing precipitation

Vapor cools, forming clouds

Invisible water vapor

Sun's heat causes evaporation

Groundwater flows into lakes and rivers

Evaporation from land and water

GO ON

In certain areas, thunderstorms and even tornadoes can result as warmer air picks up evaporating water. Warm air trying to move upward can push cold air away, creating wind or changing the wind's direction. So spring storms often bring pouring rains and heavy winds.

Spring thawing and rainfall help revive the plants and wildlife. Gardens are planted. Flowers poke out of the soil. Animals drink from rivers and streams. Life begins anew!

Try This Experiment at Home

You will need:

- a large pan or small pool
- water
- a flat area of concrete, asphalt, or soil
- thermometer

1. Check the weather forecast and choose a day when sunshine is predicted.

2. In the late afternoon or early evening, place the large pan or small pool on the concrete, asphalt, or soil. Make sure it is in an area that will not be bothered overnight and will get direct sunlight the next day.

3. Fill the pool or pan with water and leave it overnight.

4. Early the next morning, check the temperature of the water and the temperature of the surface next to the container. You may use a thermometer, or just check with your hand. Which is warmer? Record your observations.

5. In the afternoon, while the area is still receiving sunlight, check the temperature of each again. Which is warmer now? Which is heating up more quickly? Record your observations.

6. Write a conclusion about what the experiment showed you about warming land and water.

19 Based on what you read, what can you infer?

   A Conserving water is not really important.

   B Water probably cools off more slowly than land.

   C The amount of rain that falls in an area does not change with the season.

   D The longest day of the year occurs during the vernal equinox.

20 According to the passage, what causes wind patterns to change in the spring?

   A warming air

   B cooling air

   C thunderstorms

   D the hydrologic cycle

21 Read the statement below. Then answer the question that follows.

   Leaves begin to sprout on tree branches.

   Under which heading does this detail belong?

   A The Vernal Equinox

   B Signs of Spring

   C Rainfall

   D Try This Experiment at Home

22 According to the illustration, what causes clouds to form?

   A invisible water vapor

   B groundwater

   C the cooling of vapor

   D the heat of the sun

Directions: Use the "Try This Experiment at Home" directions to answer the following questions.

---

23 What is the main purpose of the experiment?

   A to check the weather forecast

   B to predict sunny weather

   C to learn about the warming of land and water

   D to learn if a surface is flat or tilted

24 When should the experiment be started?

   A in the morning

   B in the late afternoon or evening

   C after a heavy rain

   D when the weather forecast calls for clouds

GO ON

25 Where must the pan or pool of water be placed?

A in a shady spot

B in a spot that will get direct sunlight

C in a place where it is sheltered from rain

D inside, near a large window

26 The overall structure of "Try This Experiment at Home" is—

A chronological, or order of events.

B problem/solution.

C cause/effect.

D comparison/contrast.

Directions: Read the passage. Then answer the questions that follow.

Ben Carson: Miracle Worker

1 Imagine being so good at something that people from many countries come to seek your help. Dr. Ben Carson is such a person. He performs brain surgery at the world-famous Johns Hopkins Hospital in Baltimore, Maryland. His skills have saved many lives. Some of his operations have even made medical history. In 1987, he was the first surgeon to separate Siamese twins joined at the back of the head.

2 But when Ben Carson was growing up, he never dreamed he could save lives. He never thought he was smart enough to operate on people's brains. In fact, in elementary school he often was the worst student in his class.

3 Ben Carson faced many challenges when he was growing up. Learning was difficult for him because he was always trying to overcome other problems. His mother struggled to raise Ben and his brother by herself in the early 1960s. She worked long hours to keep her sons clothed and fed. Because she had to work so much, Ben and his brother weren't able to spend much time with her.

4 Another problem was that the Carsons moved many times. Once, when Ben was in fifth grade, they moved from Boston to Detroit. The children in Ben's new class were way ahead of him in every subject. He couldn't keep up. His teachers tried to help him, but nothing seemed to work.

5 Ben Carson likes to tell a story about that difficult time. One day, his teacher handed back a test. She then asked students to tell their scores to the rest of the class. When it was Ben's turn, he mumbled his score—"none." But the teacher thought he had said "nine." Nine out of ten was a wonderful score! She was excited, and went on for a long time congratulating him. Ben didn't know what to do. Finally, the student sitting behind Ben raised her hand. She told the teacher that Ben had said, "NONE," not "NINE." The teacher felt very bad about the mistake. Ben, of course, felt even worse.

6   But during these painful times there was always one person who gave Ben constant encouragement—his mother. Mrs. Carson was convinced that her sons had bright futures, and she often told them so. Ben admits, however, that he didn't always want to listen to his mother.

7   Mrs. Carson grew very unhappy hearing Ben complain about all the things he couldn't do. So she came up with a plan. She told her sons that they had to cut down their television watching and read two books per week. Since she wasn't home to supervise them all the time, they had to turn in book reports. Mrs. Carson, who only had a third grade education, could barely read the book reports. But this was a secret she didn't reveal until her sons were older.

8   Slowly, Ben grew to like reading. And slowly, he became a better student. The new knowledge helped him answer questions in class. The more he read, the more he wanted to know. In just a few years, Ben was receiving awards for his achievements.

9   High school, however, brought new troubles. His family moved again. At his new school, wearing the right clothes was very important. Ben's mother couldn't afford to buy him the clothes he wanted. He was often angry about many things and not interested in studying. The anger grew worse and worse. On one terrible day, he almost seriously wounded one of his friends. After that, he realized he had to change.

10   Ben Carson did change. He worked hard, and eventually attended some of the best colleges in the country. During this time he felt his mind could do anything. In medical school he discovered his special talent—brain surgery. Because he was very good with children, he decided to become a pediatric brain surgeon.

11   Today Dr. Carson spends most of his time performing surgery on very ill children. But he also travels all over the country telling audiences his childhood story. He tells people the amazing things their brains can do. He likes to point out that a human brain can process two million pieces of information per second. With brains like these, he says, we should never talk about what we can't do.

27   Which sentence tells the main idea of this selection?

   A Ben Carson and his brother read two books a week.

   B Ben Carson overcame many problems to become a brain surgeon.

   C Brain surgeons can separate Siamese twins.

   D Ben Carson attended some of the best colleges in the country.

GO ON

28 Explain three problems that Ben had to overcome when he was growing up. Support your answer with details from the text. (3 points)

_____

_____

_____

_____

_____

_____

_____

29 Which of the following is a minor detail and does NOT belong in a summary of this passage?

  A Ben Carson faced many challenges as a child.

  B The Carsons moved many times and Ben had trouble keeping up in school.

  C When Ben was in fifth grade, his family moved from Boston to Detroit.

  D Mrs. Carson came up with a plan to help her sons do better in school.

30 Mrs. Carson required Ben to read two books and write two book reports per week. Explain the effect of Mrs. Carson's plan on Ben. Use examples from the passage to support your answer. What do you think would have happened if she had not come up with this plan? (3 points)

_____

_____

_____

_____

_____

_____

_____

Directions: Read these passages about Annie Oakley. Then answer the questions that follow.

Annie Oakley

Annie Oakley was born in 1860 in Darke County, Ohio, and lived until 1926. She grew up to become the best sharpshooter and one of the best-known female symbols of the Old West. Annie learned to shoot as a young girl living on her stepfather's farm near Cincinnati. She had perfect aim and rarely missed a target. Annie's shooting talent helped her make money for her family, who were quite poor. She sold the rabbits and quail she hunted and quickly earned enough money to pay off the debt on the farm.

In 1875, Annie Oakley beat an expert sharpshooter named Frank Butler in a shooting contest. (Annie hit all 25 of her targets, while Mr. Butler hit only 24.) Frank and Annie married the next year, and Annie began performing with her husband in a traveling show that showed off their shooting abilities. They took their show around the Midwest, and they became famous.

In 1885, Frank and Annie joined Buffalo Bill Cody's Wild West Show. Unlike Annie, Buffalo Bill had grown up in the West and had taken part in its settlement. Bill made Annie, who had taken the name "Little Sure Shot," the star of his show. Frank became her assistant and manager but did not perform anymore. The show traveled around the United States and throughout Europe. It was very successful—in fact, one time the group even performed for the Queen of England.

Annie could do some remarkable shooting tricks. She hit targets thrown into the air by cowboys and shot out flaming candles spinning around on a wheel, all while galloping on horseback. She shot holes in a small card when it was flipped in the air. Soon, people had a new name for any ticket with holes punched in it—an "Annie Oakley."

Annie performed in the Wild West Show through 1901. She quit because she was injured in a railroad accident and had to have several operations on her back. Later, she began giving shows to raise money to help widows, orphans, and women who were suffering. At that time, most women had fewer freedoms than men did, so Annie stood out as an example. Unlike most women of her time, Annie worked, traveled, made money, and became famous. She also worked for the rights of women to hold jobs, to receive equal pay, and to take part in sports.

My Early Life

1 Mr. [Frank] Butler was traveling through Cincinnati showing off his shooting abilities with several other marksmen. He was conceited. Everywhere he went, he claimed he could outshoot anyone.

2 My brother came to me and said, "Annie, I think you can beat that man."

3 I laughed, merry with the thought of a mere slip of a girl like me challenging a man to a shooting contest. But the idea of winning $50 was enticing.

4 You can imagine Mr. Butler's reaction when he received the news that I was his

competitor. He chuckled and snorted and chortled and guffawed and soon his face was a beet, and he had to be pounded on the back to catch his breath.

5   On the day of the competition, I dressed in my best skirt and a blouse with rows of lace, and I plaited my hair and tucked it neatly under a new bonnet. Mr. Butler winked at me before he lifted his rifle. His aim was good, though not perfect, and he missed his sixteenth or seventeenth shot. My hands shook, but I took a deep breath and pushed my bonnet back so that nothing obstructed my view, and I did not miss a single shot.

6   For a second, it was absolutely quiet, but then you could hear the sound of the crowd audibly gasping.

7   A dark cloud passed over Mr. Butler's face. Then, his face broke into a smile.

8   We were married several years later, and that was the beginning of a partnership that would last for many years as we crisscrossed America and Europe performing in Buffalo Bill's Wild West Show.

www.Photos.com

31 Based upon the context of paragraph 3 of "My Early Life," the word <u>enticing</u> means—

A tempting.

B difficult.

C crazy.

D upsetting.

32 Use the dictionary entry to answer the following question.

> **game** *n.* **1.** a sporting event **2.** a contest **3.** animals hunted for food or sport *adj.* **4.** willing or ready

Annie, as everyone called her, began hunting <u>game</u> for her hungry family.

Which definition fits the way <u>game</u> is used in the sentence above?

A definition 1

B definition 2

C definition 3

D definition 4

33 How does the picture help you understand what you read in the passages? (1 point)

_____

_____

_____

34 What detail do you learn from "My Early Life" that you don't find in "Annie Oakley"?

  A Annie eventually married Frank Butler.

  B Annie won the shooting contest with Frank Butler.

  C Annie performed in Buffalo Bill's Wild West Show.

  D Annie won $50 in the shooting contest.

35 Contrast the description of the shooting contest found in both passages. Give details from the text to explain how they are different. Which one is more interesting? (5 points)

_____

_____

_____

_____

_____

_____

_____

_____

Take a break. Then go on to Part 3.

GO ON

Directions: Read each question and choose the best answer.

36 Choose the sentence in which a word is NOT spelled correctly.

   A We have had four cloudy days in a row.
   B Erica did not pack enough food in the picnic basket.
   C Can you see through the fog?
   D Don't trip on that pile of would!

37 Complete the sentence below by choosing the word that is spelled correctly.

   The _____ of the ceiling is ten feet.

   A height   **C** hieght
   B heighth   **D** hight

38 Complete the sentence below by choosing the word that is spelled correctly.

   How much _____ is in your pocket?

   A monie   **C** moniy
   B mony   **D** money

39 Which sentence uses capitalization correctly?

   A Grandma works for East Shore power company.
   B Her job is to tell people how to save Energy.
   C She visited my school on march 13.
   D Principal Brenton introduced her to everyone.

40 Read the sentence below.

   The lesson of the story is to not be greedy.

   Which of the following is a prepositional phrase?

   A The lesson
   B of the story
   C is to not
   D not be greedy

41 She is the girl _____ sits next to me in class.

   A who
   B which
   C where
   D why

42 Which of the following sentences places adjectives in the correct order?

   A The old little lady was crossing the street.

   B She wore a big blue hat.

   C In the hat was a green and red long feather.

   D The lady carried a wooden tall cane.

43 Yesterday I _____ on the sidewalk when a car almost hit me!

   A am walking

   B are walking

   C was walking

   D will be walking

44 Which of the following sentences uses correct capitalization?

   A The united states celebrates its independence on July 4.

   B On that date in 1776 the *declaration of independence* was signed.

   C The signing of this document caused the Revolutionary War.

   D The american army eventually defeated the british army.

45 Do you know the reason _____ the plummer is here?

   A why   **C** who

   B where   **D** when

46 Which sentence is punctuated correctly?

   A "Are you ready." Mom asked

   B "Are you ready?" Mom asked.

   C "Are you ready," Mom asked?

   D "Are you ready, Mom asked.

47 Which of the following sentences is correct?

   A The marine biologist explained, "About fish."

   B She said, "Many fish are able to fool their enemies.

   C She added "Many fish can change their color."

   D She explained, "They can match the ocean floor perfectly."

48 Which of the following compound sentences is correctly punctuated?

   A Ostriches are birds but they don't fly

   B Ostriches can't fly, but they can run very quickly.

   C An ostrich's wings are tiny; and they can't lift their big bodies.

   D Their legs seem skinny and weak yet they can kick hard enough to break a lion's back.

49 I heard about the tornado that hit your town. You _____ terrified!

    A might have been

    B should have been

    C could have been

    D must have been

50 Write a complete sentence explaining where you are right now. Use at least one prepositional phrase. Underline the prepositional phrase. (1 point)

_____

_____

_____

51 The paragraph below contains one sentence fragment and one run-on sentence. Rewrite the paragraph correctly on the lines below. Be sure to use correct capitalization and punctuation. (2 points)

> Fire ants first arrived in the United States from South America about 50 years ago. Live in the southern states but are beginning to move north. Fire ants cause lots of damage these ants destroy crops and sting people.

_____

_____

_____

_____

_____

STOP

Points Earned/Total = _____/70

26

Reading Literature Lesson 1

Explain and Infer

Review the Standard (RL.4.1, W.4.9)
- **Refer** to details in a text
- Draw **inferences** from a text

Q: What does "**referring** to details" mean?

A: "**Referring** to details" means that you use facts from a story when you write or talk about a story. In the sentence *Mary is mean because her mother has died,* the fact that her mother has died is a detail from the story.

Q: How do I make an **inference** about a text?

A: When you make an **inference**, or infer something from a text, you are making a good guess. You must use the information from the story and also what you already know.

Example: Ahmad stomped up the stairs to his room. "I'm never going back to school again!" he yelled, as he slammed his door.

From Ahmad's actions and words, you can infer that something bad happened at school, and he is very angry.

 Try It

Directions: Read the following passage. Then answer the questions that follow.

Mr. Cruz stood at the entrance to the science museum. He held his finger to his lips until his students were quiet. "Boys and girls," he said, "please stay together so that no one gets lost in the museum."

At first Juana didn't have any trouble keeping up with her class. The rock room and the insect room didn't interest her very much. Then Mr. Cruz led the class into the dinosaur room. Juana gasped. One of the dinosaur skeletons was taller than her

GO ON

house! Juana stared at the skeleton for a long time. She had never seen anything like this before. Then she asked, "Mr. Cruz, what ever happened to the dinosaurs?"

No one answered. Juana looked around and realized that her class was gone. "Now I'm lost," she said to herself, wondering what she would do next. But just then, she noticed a friendly-looking museum guard standing by the doorway.

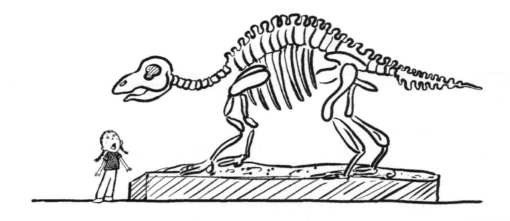

1   Why did Mr. Cruz hold his finger to his lips? Use details from the passage to support your answer. (1 point)

_____

_____

_____

2   When Juana saw the huge skeleton, she felt—

   A bored.

   B amazed.

   C sorry.

   D worried.

Example 1 asks you to think about why Mr. Cruz held his finger to his lips. If you **refer** back to the passage, you will find a detail that explains the reason. Mr. Cruz held his finger to his lips "until his students were quiet." A good answer will include this detail. Remember to use quotation marks around any words that are directly from the story.

Good: *The passage says that Mr. Cruz held his finger to his lips "until his students were quiet." Mr. Cruz was trying to signal to his class that they needed to stop talking.*

A poor answer will not refer to details from the text.

Poor: *Mr. Cruz wanted his students to stop talking.*

Example 2 asks you to make an **inference** about a character in the story. You must use clues in the story to decide how Juana felt when she saw the huge skeleton. The passage says that the skeleton was "taller than her house," and Juana had "never seen anything like this before." Juana was probably *amazed* by such a sight. **Choice B** is correct.

◎ Try It On Your Own

3   Which detail from the story hints that Juana may get separated from her class?

   A *At first Juana didn't have any trouble keeping up with her class.*
   B *The rock room and the insect room didn't interest her very much.*
   C *Juana gasped.*
   D *Juana looked around and realized that her class was gone.*

4   At the end of the story, we can infer that Juana will probably—

   A pretend she is not lost.
   B explore the museum alone.
   C stay in the dinosaur room.
   D ask the guard for help.

Reading Literature
Lesson 2

Character, Setting, and Plot

Review the Standard (RL.4.3)

• Describe a **character**, **setting**, or **event**

Q: What are **characters**, the **setting**, and **events** in a story?

A: Understanding the **characters**, the **setting**, and the plot, or **events** in the story, will help you understand the entire story.

Term	Definition	Example
Character	The people or animals whom the story is about	Little Red Riding Hood, the wolf, and Grandma are all characters in the story "Little Red Riding Hood."
Setting	The time and place where the events in the story happen	The forest, Grandma's house, early in the morning
Plot	Events in the story that center around a problem or conflict	Little Red Riding Hood sets off to take some food to her sick grandmother. As she walked through the woods, she met a wolf.

Q: How can I describe a character, the setting, or the events in a story?

A: You must always refer back to details from the story to describe the characters, the setting, or the plot. Sometimes graphic organizers can be helpful when giving details about the story.

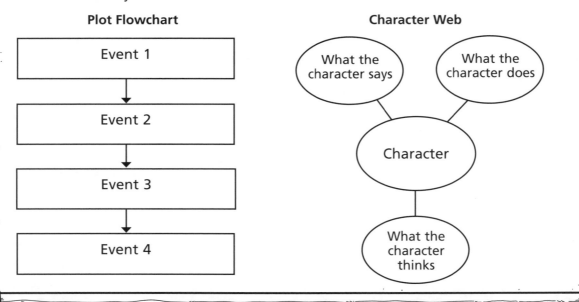

Plot Flowchart

Event 1 → Event 2 → Event 3 → Event 4

Character Web

What the character says — What the character does — Character — What the character thinks

Directions: Read the following passage. Then answer the questions that follow.

The Science Project

"So, Jimmy, have you figured out what your project for the science fair will be?" asked Jimmy's father at the supper table one evening.

"Sort of," Jimmy answered quietly.

Jimmy's father was confused. "What do you mean, 'sort of'?"

"Well, I think maybe I'll do something about toys that run on solar power," Jimmy mumbled. "But I don't know for sure," he answered, looking down at his hands.

"That sounds interesting. Tell me more about your project," said his father.

Jimmy explained that they were studying solar energy in his science class. One day while playing, he had an idea: using solar energy to power toys.

"What do you have so far?" Jimmy's father asked. He continued to ask Jimmy questions, and Jimmy answered eagerly, encouraged by his father's interest. "It sounds like you already have several possibilities in mind," his father said after a moment. "Have you experimented with any of them?"

"I've made some drawings. But I haven't really tried anything out," responded Jimmy. "I'm not sure whether I have a good idea or not."

"I think you have a great idea," his father replied.

"But what if it doesn't work?" Jimmy asked. He was a little worried about his project.

"You won't know if it will work until you try. Do you have what you need to get started?" asked his father.

Jimmy thought for a minute. "What do I need? Hmm. Most of the stuff is around the house. But I do need a few things from the hardware store. Maybe you could drive me there tomorrow?" Jimmy asked excitedly.

"You bet! Why don't you make a list of the things you need?" said Jimmy's father.

"That'll be easy!" shouted Jimmy eagerly.

---

1 Which word best describes Jimmy at the beginning of the story?

   A eager

   B uncertain

   C smart

   D angry

2 Where does this story take place?

    A at the hardware store on Saturday

    B in Jimmy's bedroom at bedtime

    C at supper time in Jimmy's house

    D early in the morning at school

3 Study the following chart.

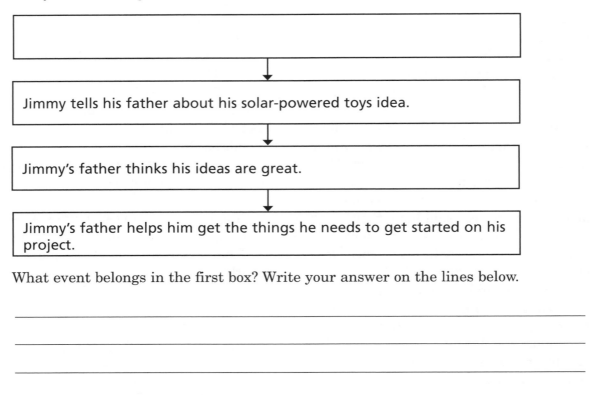

What event belongs in the first box? Write your answer on the lines below.

_____

_____

_____

_____

    Example 1 asks about the main **character** in the story, Jimmy. To answer the question, you need to think about what Jimmy says, thinks, and does at the beginning of the story. When Jimmy's father asks him if he has figured out his science project, Jimmy says "sort of." Later he says, "But I don't know for sure." The only answer that makes sense is **choice B**, *uncertain*.

    Example 2 is a question about **setting**, or where the story takes place. In the first paragraph, the author says that Jimmy and his father are at the supper table. This identifies the setting—at home, at supper time. **Choice C** is correct.

    To answer **Example 3**, you must think about the **events** in the story, or the plot. The flowchart is missing the first event in the story. This event is the cause of all the other events. A close look at the story reveals that the first thing that happened in the plot was that Jimmy's dad asked him about his science fair project. Be sure to write your answer in a complete sentence.

    Good: *Jimmy's dad asks him if he has figured out what his science fair project will be.*

◎ Try It On Your Own

4 Based on what he does in the story, Jimmy's father can be described as—

   A helpful.

   B strict.

   C talkative.

   D bossy.

5 What problem does Jimmy face in the story?

   A His father is angry at him.

   B He can't answer his father's questions.

   C He isn't sure if his project idea is a good one.

   D He can't think of a way to get the stuff he needs.

6 How does Jimmy's character change from the beginning to the end of the story? Be sure to use details from the passage to support your answer. (3 points)

_____

_____

_____

_____

_____

_____

_____

_____

Theme and Summary

Review the Standard (RL.4.2)

- Determine a **theme** of a story, drama, or poem
- **Summarize** the text

Q: What is a **theme** of a story, drama, or poem?

A: The **theme** of a story is the main idea the author wants to communicate. Some stories tell you the moral, or lesson, such as "Be satisfied with what you have." Usually you must figure out the main idea by thinking about the characters, the problem the characters face, and how the problem ends, or resolves. Some good questions to ask are:

- How does the main character change from the beginning to the end of the story?
- How does the main character overcome the problem in the story?
- What lesson does the character learn?

Q: How do I **summarize** a text?

A: A good **summary** will include the major events in the story. It should not include minor, or unimportant, details.

 Try It

Directions: Read the following passage. Then answer the questions that follow.

The Story of Arachne

A Greek Myth

Arachne was a young woman who had a great talent. She could weave such beautiful cloth that people came from miles around to watch her. But Arachne was too proud. She often bragged about her weaving. She even claimed that she was a better weaver than the goddess Minerva.

Now Minerva was the goddess of many skills, including spinning, weaving, and needlework. When she heard Arachne bragging she decided to give her some friendly advice. Disguised as an old woman, she paid the young weaver a visit.

"If you say you are sorry for what you have said," she told Arachne, "the goddess Minerva will forgive you."

But Arachne would not take back her words. "If Minerva is such a great weaver let her come down here and show what she can do. I can beat her in any weaving contest."

At this Minerva threw off her disguise and brought out her loom. The weaving contest began. Minerva wove designs that showed what had happened to other humans who challenged the gods. But Arachne wove pictures showing some of the foolish things the gods had done.

Minerva saw that Arachne was a great weaver, but she was outraged at the pictures she wove. So she punished the proud young woman by turning her into a spider. Arachne would never enjoy the life of a human again. But ever since then, spiders have spun beautiful webs.

1 Write a summary of the story. Be sure to include only the major events. (3 points)

_____

_____

_____

_____

_____

2 Which word BEST describes Arachne?

A kind

B eager

C beautiful

D proud

3 One of the themes of the story is—

A hide your talent.

B spiders are bad.

C pride can get you in trouble.

D goddesses are jealous.

For **Example 1**, you need to write a **summary** of the story. It may be helpful to go back to the story and underline the main action that happens in each paragraph. You should also include the main characters and setting in the story.

Good: *Arachne was a very talented weaver. She bragged that she was a better weaver than the goddess Minerva. Minerva disguised herself as an old woman, visited Arachne and told her that the gods would forgive her if she asked for forgiveness. But Arachne refused and challenged Minerva to a weaving contest. Arachne wove pictures of the foolish things that the gods had done. Then Minerva punished Arachne by changing her into a spider. That is why spiders weave beautiful webs.*

GO ON

A poor answer will contain incorrect information or unimportant details in the wrong order.

Poor: *Spiders weave beautiful webs. Arachne was the first spider. She was turned into a spider by Minerva. Minerva heard Arachne bragging about being a better weaver than she was. They had a weaving contest.*

For **Example 2**, you must think about the character of Arachne. When you consider the details of the story, you see that Arachne was very proud. These details include that she bragged about her weaving, she claimed she could beat Minerva in a weaving contest, and she wove pictures showing some of the foolish things the gods had done. The correct answer is **choice D**.

To answer **Example 3**, you must decide which answer is a **theme** of the story. You understand theme by looking at the characters, the problem the character faces, and how the characters change. In the story, Arachne is too proud and she makes the gods angry. Although Minerva tries to warn her, Arachne doesn't listen, and Minerva turns her into a spider. From these details, we can conclude that one of the themes of the story is **choice C**, *pride can get you in trouble*.

◎ Try It On Your Own

Directions: Read the following passage. Then answer the questions that follow.

Jim and Aunt Pat did not talk much as they drove down Beacon Street toward the city park. Jim was too busy thinking about pitching in the last baseball game of the summer. If his team won the game, they would be the city champions. Aunt Pat was Jim's biggest fan, and she knew how nervous he was about the game. She had promised to get Jim to the park for an early practice. Lou, the team catcher, was going to meet Jim there so they could warm up together.

Suddenly Jim heard a loud pop, and the car swerved. Aunt Pat pulled the car over to the side of the road. "We've got a flat tire," she said. "It's going to take me a while to change it."

Jim stood next to the car as Aunt Pat pulled a spare tire and some tools out of the trunk. He waited silently as his aunt started to remove the flat tire. Then he looked at his watch and sighed. Aunt Pat looked up at him. "Try not to get upset, Jim," she said. "I'll be finished soon. Everything will be fine."

As she spoke, another car pulled up behind them. Lou and his father got out of the car. Jim's face brightened when he saw them. "Boy, am I ever glad to see you!" he cried.

"Lou to the rescue," Aunt Pat said, smiling as she stood up. "You three go on ahead to the park. You don't want to be late. I'll get there before the game starts."

4   Which of these details does NOT belong in a summary of the passage?

A Aunt Pat is driving Jim to his baseball game.

B Aunt Pat is Jim's biggest fan.

C Aunt Pat's car gets a flat tire on their way to the game.

D Lou and his father give Jim a ride to the park.

5 In your own words, write a summary of this story. Be sure to include only the most important details in your summary. (3 points)

_____

_____

_____

_____

_____

_____

6 Explain the theme, or main idea, of the story. Be sure to support your answer with specific details from the passage. (3 points)

_____

_____

_____

_____

_____

_____

Test-Taking Tips

1 Watch for questions that require you to give details from the text. Make sure to include specific ideas that support your answer.

2 To answer questions about theme, look for details in the story that suggest there is a lesson to be learned. Ask the questions: How does the main character change from the beginning of the story to the end? What lesson does he or she learn?

3 When summarizing a story, be sure to include the main idea of the entire passage and any important events. A summary should be shorter than the passage you are summarizing.

4 An inference is an educated guess based upon what the text says and also what you know to be true. You have to go beyond the text to find the answer.

Go for it!

Unit One Practice Test

Estimated time: 20 minutes

Directions: Read the following passage. Then answer the questions that follow.

Improving Mr. Twine

Jake's neighbor, Mr. Twine, was very nice. He always smiled and greeted the people he met on the sidewalk. But Mr. Twine was very peculiar too. Sometimes Mr. Twine would do the strangest things.

He had a habit of going into the grocery store to pick up his mail. Sometimes he would go into the post office to buy his groceries. Mr. Twine was never quite sure whom he was talking to. Once he had stopped Jake and his dad in their driveway to talk. He asked Jake how work was, and then he asked Jake's father about neighborhood baseball games.

Jake sometimes wondered what was wrong with Mr. Twine. Then one day, Jake met Mr. Twine near the library.

"Good morning, Mr. Twine," Jake greeted him.

"Jake, is that you? Well, hello there," replied Mr. Twine as he squinted at Jake.

"Yes, it's me!" was Jake's reply. "Look at the great books I just got at the library."

Mr. Twine peered at the books and turned them around in his hands. He even held one upside down for a moment and tried to read it. Jake thought about that episode all afternoon. That's when he figured out what Mr. Twine's problem was.

"Do you think Mr. Twine may need glasses?" Jake asked his parents later that evening.

"That would explain his odd behavior," answered Jake's mother.

"It sure would," his father agreed.

The very next day, Jake asked Mr. Twine if he needed glasses.

"Heavens, no!" Mr. Twine said strongly. "I can see quite well."

But Jake was not convinced. He talked to Mr. Twine about the benefits of wearing glasses. He mentioned it every day for two weeks. He told Mr. Twine that lenses to correct vision had been around since the thirteenth century. Even then, people wore the lenses in frames. Jake also told Mr. Twine about Benjamin Franklin. In 1784, Franklin invented bifocal lenses so that people could see things far away as well as objects close by.

"Just give it a try," encouraged Jake.

Over time, Jake convinced Mr. Twine that he really did need glasses. Mr. Twine agreed to see an eye doctor. The glasses arrived the very next day, and Mr. Twine was thrilled.

Mr. Twine knew just where the post office and grocery stores were. He recognized every person he met along the sidewalk. He could tell Jake and his father apart.

"Glasses are the greatest invention in the world!" Mr. Twine told Jake when he saw him walking across the front yard toward his house. "Thank you, Jake. Thank you for encouraging me to go to the eye doctor. You are certainly a good neighbor."

Jake smiled when he saw how happy Mr. Twine was. That night, Mr. Twine took Jake and his parents to see a movie. It was his way of showing how grateful he was to Jake.

1 Which of the following does NOT describe a setting in this passage?

   A Jake's front yard

   B the eye doctor's office

   C near the library

   D the sidewalk outside Jake's house

2 What problem does Jake face in this passage?

   A He doesn't like his neighbor, Mr. Twine.

   B He needs to learn more about Benjamin Franklin.

   C He doesn't think Mr. Twine is a good neighbor.

   D He needs to find a way to convince Mr. Twine to get glasses.

3 Which sentence from the story helps you infer that Jake is worried about Mr. Twine?

   A *Jake smiled when he saw how happy Mr. Twine was.*

   B *Jake thought about that episode all afternoon.*

   C *Over time, Jake convinced Mr. Twine that he really did need glasses.*

   D *Then one day, Jake met Mr. Twine near the library.*

4 Which sentence best describes the theme of the passage?

   A People who are peculiar do not make good neighbors.

   B Glasses have been around since the thirteenth century.

   C Good neighbors leave one another alone.

   D Good neighbors help one another.

5 This web shows details about Jake. Use the web to answer the question.

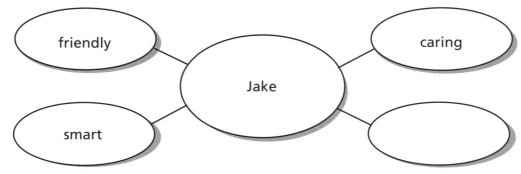

Which word belongs in the empty circle?

   A angry

   B lazy

   C polite

   D quiet

6 Write a summary of the story. (3 points)

_____

_____

_____

_____

_____

_____

_____

_____

_____

_____

Points Earned/Total = _____/8

Reading Literature Lesson 4

Word Choice

Review the Standards (RL.4.4, L.4.5, L.4.5.a, L.4.5.b)

- Determine the meaning of **allusions**, **idioms**, **adages**, and **proverbs**
- Demonstrate understanding of simple **similes** and **metaphors**
- Understand **nuances** in word meanings

Q: What are **allusions**, **idioms**, **adages**, and **proverbs**?

A: Sometimes writers use words or phrases that mean something different from the literal, or actual, meaning of the words. Sometimes these types of phrases are called *figurative language.* To understand figurative language, ask yourself, *What does the writer mean? What is the writer trying to communicate?* Study this chart.

Figurative Language	Definition	Example	Meaning
Allusion	a reference to another story or myth	Cleaning out the garage was a <u>Herculean task</u>.	In Greek mythology, Hercules had to complete a series of very difficult tasks. A *Herculean task* is one that is very hard.
Idiom	an expression that means something very different from the meanings of the individual words	The test was <u>a piece of cake</u>.	The test was very easy.
Adage/proverb	a saying that contains truth or wisdom about life	Don't count your chickens before they are hatched.	Don't be too sure of something that hasn't happened yet.

GO ON

Simile	figurative language that compares two unlike things using *like* or *as*	Cammie was <u>as bold as a lion</u> as she went up to the bully and told him to stop picking on the little kid.	Cammie was not afraid of the bully. She was bold and confident like a lion.
Metaphor	figurative language that compares two unlike things by saying that one thing is another	<u>Alonzo was a jet,</u> flying around the bases.	Alonzo was going so fast around the bases that he seemed like a jet.
Personification	giving human actions to a nonhuman object	The wind <u>sang a low, sad song.</u>	The wind made a noise that sounded like a person singing a song.

Q: What are **nuances** in word meanings?

A: A **nuance** in word meanings is a slight difference between what two words mean. For example, think about the words *warm* and *hot*. They mean almost the same thing, but *hot* means something has greater heat than something *warm*. Think about the nuances in the words *cheap* and *inexpensive*. What is the difference between saying *I think the movie is at 4:00 PM* and *I know the movie is at 4:00 PM*?

⮕ Try It

Directions: Read the following passage. Then answer the questions that follow.

1   Tony sat at the table in his grandfather's restaurant with a drawing pad on his lap. From time to time, he looked up at a man who was eating his breakfast at the next table. The man's hair was as white as snow, and his face was a spider's web of lines. Tony's pencil danced across the paper as he drew the man's face.

2   Tony heard his father calling him. Like a rocket, he dropped his pad and <u>hurried</u> into the kitchen. "Grandpa and I need some help in here," his father said. "Bring up some bread from downstairs. Then start washing these breakfast dishes so we'll be ready for lunch." As Tony started down the stairs, he heard his father say, "Dad, I just don't know what to do with that boy. He'll never learn how to work in this restaurant. He always has his head in the clouds. He's always <u>dreaming</u> about being an artist."

3   A few minutes later, Tony came back upstairs with the bread. With his hand on Tony's shoulder, Grandpa said in a kind, gentle voice, "Never mind what your father says. Sure it's important to help out around here and learn how to work, but you have a talent. You're going to be a fine artist. Someday your father will see that. So no matter what happens, don't give up on your dream."

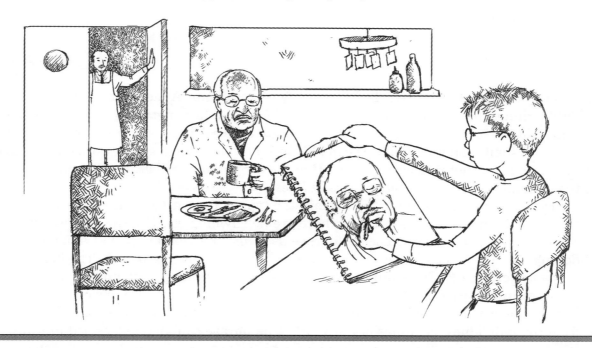

1   Which phrase is an example of a metaphor?

   A *The man's hair was as white as snow*

   B *his face was a spider's web of lines*

   C *Tony's pencil danced across the paper*

   D *dreaming about being an artist*

2   Reread the following sentence from the passage.

   Like a rocket, he dropped his pad and hurried into the kitchen.

   The words <u>like a rocket</u> are an example of which type of figurative language?

   A rhyming   **C** a metaphor

   B a simile   **D** personification

3   Explain the meaning of the phrase, "He always has his head in the clouds."

   _____

   _____

   _____

4 Read the following sentence from the story.

Like a rocket, he dropped his pad and <u>hurried</u> into the kitchen.

Which of the following has nearly the same meaning as the word *hurried* in the sentence?

A rushed

B walked

C moved

D hopped

In **Example 1**, you are asked to identify a **metaphor**. A metaphor compares unlike things, but it does not use the words *like* or *as*. In a metaphor, the author says something is something else. You can eliminate choice A because it uses the word *as*, so it is a simile. Choices C and D can also be eliminated because the words do not say something is something else. **Choice B** is the correct answer because the author says the old man's face *was a spider's web of lines*.

In **Example 2**, you are asked explain the type of figurative language being used. You can eliminate choice A because there are no rhyming words in the phrase. You can eliminate choice C because the phrase uses *like,* and you know that a metaphor doesn't use *like* or *as.* Choice D is not correct because Tony is a person. The best answer is **choice B**. The simile tells you that Tony is moving very quickly.

Example 3 asks you to explain the meaning of the phrase, "He always has his head in the clouds." This is an **idiom** because the phrase means something different from the individual meanings of the words. The phrase can't be understood literally. It doesn't mean that Tony is tall enough for his head to reach the clouds. Use the context to help you figure out the meaning. Tony's dad is complaining that he isn't working and instead he is daydreaming. So the phrase means that Tony is always thinking about other things instead of doing his job. A good answer will contain details from the text.

Good: *"He always has his head in the clouds" means that Tony is not focused on the things he needs to get done. Instead Tony is daydreaming about being an artist.*

A poor answer will incorrectly explain the phrase or will not give details from the text.

Poor: *The phrase means that Tony wants to go outside and play instead of doing his work.*

For **Example 4** you must think about the **nuances**, or the slight difference in meanings of words. The word *hurried* means to move quickly. Decide which answer choice has nearly the same meaning as *hurried*. It may be helpful to read the sentence replacing the word *hurried* with each answer choice. Try to picture what is happening as you read each new sentence. By doing this, you will conclude that the word *rushed* means nearly the same as the word *hurried*. **Choice A** is correct.

5 What is one comparison the author makes in this passage?

   A The author compares the old man's shirt to snow.

   B The author compares the old man's hair to snow.

   C The author compares the old man to Tony's grandfather.

   D The author compares Tony to the old man.

6 Reread the following sentence from the passage.

Tony's pencil danced across the paper as he drew the man's face.

What does this sentence mean?

   A Tony almost dropped his pencil.

   B Tony drew a picture of a race.

   C Tony drew very quickly and easily.

   D Tony drew very slowly and steadily.

7 Which of the following proverbs fits with Tony's grandpa's words at the end of the story?

   A The future belongs to those who believe in the beauty of their dreams.

   B A bird in the hand is worth two in the bush.

   C Slow and steady wins the race.

   D Spare the rod, spoil the child.

8 Read the following sentence from the passage.

He's always dreaming about being an artist.

Which of the following words has nearly the same meaning as the word dreaming?

   A planning

   B plotting

   C imagining

   D guessing

Reading Literature Lesson 5

Poetry

Review the Standard (RL.4.5)

- Explain major differences between **poems**, **drama**, and **prose**
- Refer to the parts of poems

Q: What are the major differences between **poetry**, **drama**, and **prose**?

A: Most writing is **prose**. Short stories, books, and essays are prose. Writing that is not prose is **poetry**. Poetry is usually shorter than prose. It communicates strong emotions and sometimes uses rhyme or meter. **Drama** is written to be performed by actors on a stage.

Genre	Characteristics
Fiction	This is a story that isn't true. It usually includes characters, a setting, a problem, and a solution. Examples are short stories and novels.
Poetry	Poetry often has short lines that contain rhythm, rhyme, or both. Poetry expresses ideas, experiences, and feelings. The words of a poem are chosen for the beauty of their sound as well as their meaning.
Drama	This is a story that actors perform. It includes characters, a setting, a problem, a solution, stage directions, and dialogue. It is also called a *play*.

Q: What are *meter, rhythm, verse,* and *rhyme,* and how are they used in poetry?

A: These are all terms we use when talking about poetry. Study the following example poem and the chart on the next page.

Listen, my children, and you shall hear,

Of the midnight ride of Paul Revere

On the eighteenth of April, in Seventy-five;

Hardly a man is now alive

Who remembers that famous day and year.

Term	Definition	Example from Poem
Rhyme	end of words that sound the same	hear/Revere/year five/alive
Verse/stanza	lines of poetry grouped together	Five lines are grouped together making a stanza, or verse. The example above shows one stanza of the poem.
Meter	groups of stressed (strong) and unstressed (weak) syllables that create a pattern of sound when read aloud	**Lis**ten my **child**ren and **you** shall **hear** Of the **mid**night **ride** of **Paul** Re**vere**. The word parts in bold are stressed. Each line has four stressed syllables.

 Try It

Directions: Read the following poem. Then answer the questions that follow.

Windy Nights

by Robert Louis Stevenson

1 Whenever the moon and stars are set,
2 Whenever the wind is high,
3 All night long in the dark and wet,
4 A man goes riding by.
5 Late in the night when the fires are out,
6 Why does he gallop and gallop about?

7 Whenever the trees are crying aloud,
8 And the ships are tossed at sea,
9 By, on the highway, low and loud,
10 By at the gallop goes he.
11 By at the gallop he goes, and then
12 By he comes back at the gallop again.

GO ON

1 Reread line 1 from the poem.

Whenever the moon and stars are set,

Which line ryhmes with line 1?

A *Whenever the wind is high,*
B *All night long in the dark and wet,*
C *A man goes riding by.*
D *Late in the night when the fires are out,*

2 How many stanzas are in the poem?

A 1
B 2
C 10
D 12

3 Read line 6 from the poem.

Why does he gallop and gallop about?

Which line has the same pattern of strong and weak beats?

A *Whenever the wind is high,*
B *And the ships are tossed at sea,*
C *By at the gallop goes he.*
D *By he comes back at the gallop again.*

In **Example 1** you must identify the line that rhymes with line 1. To do this, find the line that ends with a word that sounds the same as the last word of line 1, *set*. The last word of choice B, *wet*, rhymes with *set*. **Choice B** is correct.

Poems are often arranged in verses, or stanzas. **Example 2** asks you how many stanzas are in "Windy Nights." In the poem, lines 1–6 make up one stanza. A blank line separates this stanza from the next one, made up of lines 7–12. The poem has 2 stanzas. The correct answer is **choice B**.

Example 3 is a question about rhythm, or meter. The rhythm in a line of poetry is its pattern of strong and weak beats. As you say the line aloud, listen for which syllables are stressed (strong) and which are unstressed (weak). In the poem, line 6 has ten syllables, beginning with a stressed beat. The meter of the line is shown below with the stressed syllables in boldfaced type. The unstressed, or weak, syllables are in regular type.

Why does he **gal**lop and **gal**lop a**bout**?

The line has four stressed syllables, with two unstressed syllables in between. (Did you notice that when you read it aloud, it sounds like a horse's hooves?) The only choice that has the same number of syllables and the same pattern of strong and weak beats is **choice D**.

By he comes **back** at the **gal**lop a**gain**.

◎ Try It On Your Own

Directions: Read the following passage. Then answer the questions that follow.

from Daffodils
by William Wordsworth

www.photos.com

1 I wandered lonely as a cloud
2 That floats on high o'er vales and hills,
3 When all at once I saw a crowd,
4 A host, of golden daffodils,
5 Beside the lake, beneath the trees,
6 Fluttering and dancing in the breeze.

4   Which line from the poem rhymes with line 2?

   A line 3

   B line 4

   C line 5

   D line 6

5   Each line has _____ stressed, or strong syllables.

   A one

   B two

   C three

   D four

6   How does the poem describe the daffodils? Give specific details in your answer.
(3 points)

_____

_____

_____

_____

_____

_____

Reading Literature
Lesson 6

Drama

Review the Standard (RL.4.5)

- Explain major differences between **poems**, **drama**, and **prose**
- Refer to the parts of drama when writing about a text

Q: What important terms do I need to understand when I read **drama**?

A: Remember that **drama** is meant to be performed for an audience. The playwright will often give special directions to help you understand who the characters are and what is happening in the play.

Term	Definition	Example
Cast of characters	• list of characters in a play • usually includes a short description	Laura Ingalls—ten years old Mary Ingalls—Laura's older sister Ma Ingalls—Laura and Mary's mother
Setting	• where the action takes place • may also describe what the stage looks like	Setting: the Ingalls' cabin
Dialogue	• talking between two characters	LAURA: I want to go down to the river and play. MA: Not until your chores are done.
Stage directions	• directions for the actor • enclosed in parentheses • not supposed to be read aloud	LAURA: (*moving to the door*) I'm done with my chores. I'm going to the river, Ma!
Act	• part of a play • numbered ACT I, ACT II, Act III • Acts are divided into Scenes	ACT I, Scene 5

Try It

Directions: Read the selection. Then answer the questions that follow.

from the play
Courage on the Oregon Trail

ACT II, Scene 2

The wagons have stopped for the night. The Fletchers are sitting around their campfire. PETER LEE *enters, jingling the buckles on his leather bag.*

RUTHIE: What's in the bag?

LUKE (*looking into the bag*): Scissors. Razors. Combs. Looks like barber tools to me.

PETER: Right. I'm setting up a barbershop when I reach Oregon. I'm tired of Indian scouting and fur trapping.

LUKE: Where'd you learn barbering?

PETER: On a cotton plantation. I gave many of my people haircuts before I escaped from my master. Then I worked for a fur trader. I saved my money and bought barber tools. (LUKE *and* RUTHIE *stare at the shiny tools.*) Luke, I'll make a deal with you.

LUKE: What kind of deal?

PETER: You talk to every wagon driver. Tell them to come see me if they want a haircut. I'll give them a special rate—only 10 cents. I'll give you half the money.

(LUKE *hesitates, but then runs off to talk to the other men.* PETER *joins the Fletchers around the campfire while he waits for* LUKE.)

---

1 Where does this scene take place?

   A at a campfire along the Oregon Trail
   B at a barbershop
   C in Oregon
   D in a moving wagon on the Oregon Trail

2 Which of the following sentences is NOT spoken in the play?

   A *Where'd you learn barbering?*
   B *LUKE and RUTHIE stare at the shiny tools.*
   C *Luke, I'll make a deal with you.*
   D *What kind of deal?*

3   If you were directing this scene in the play, what would the character of Peter Lee look like? What would he need for his costume and props? Refer to parts of the drama to support your answer. (3 points)

_____

_____

_____

_____

_____

Example 1 asks where the scene takes place. Clues to the setting can be found in the title of the play, stage directions, and dialogue. **Choice A** is correct.

To answer **Example 2**, you must find the sentence that is not spoken in the play. Choices A, C, and D are all lines of dialogue, so they are spoken in the play. Choice B appears in the text, but it is a direction to the actors, so it is not spoken. **Choice B** is correct.

Example 3 asks you to think about what Peter Lee would look like. First, you know that he is an escaped slave, so he is an African American. The stage directions say he is carrying a bag of barber tools. He would also probably be poor, so his clothes might be old and worn. A good answer will include these details.

Good: *Because the character of Peter Lee is an escaped slave, he would be played by an African American. The stage directions say that he has a bag of barber tools. He would be dressed in clothes that would be appropriate for the pioneer days because the scene takes place on the Oregon Trail. He is probably poor, so his clothes would be old and worn.*

A poor answer would contain incorrect information or not refer to the details of the text.

Poor: *Peter Lee would be dressed like a barber.*

◎ Try It On Your Own

4   Peter Lee talks about becoming a barber in—

    A Act I, Scene 2

    B Act II, Scene 2

    C Scene 2

    D Act III, Scene 2

5   The stage directions show that Ruthie and Luke are—

    A angry that Peter has joined their campfire.

    B upset that Peter is an escaped slave.

    C orphans with no other family.

    D curious about Peter and his bag of tools.

6 Based upon the dialogue and the stage directions, how do you think Luke feels about helping Peter? Support your answer with details from the text. (3 points)

_____

_____

_____

_____

_____

_____

_____

_____

_____

_____

_____

_____

7 Which of the following will you find in a play but NOT in a short story?

    A characters

    B dialogue

    C stage directions

    D a setting

Test-Taking Tips

1 Figurative language is not meant to be taken literally. For example, someone who says, "This video game is a dinosaur" does not mean that the game is really a prehistoric beast. He or she is using a metaphor that means the game is really old and out-of-date.

2 Poetry often uses rhyme and rhythm. It tends to be shorter and communicates intense emotions. Drama is meant to be performed on a stage with characters speaking lines of dialogue. The term _prose_ refers to texts that are not poetry.

Go for it!

Unit Two Practice Test

Estimated time: 20 minutes

Directions: Read the following passage and then answer the questions that follow.

The Caterpillar
by Christina Rossetti

1 Brown and furry
2 Caterpillar in a hurry,
3 Take your walk
4 To the shady leaf, or stalk,
5 Or what not,
6 Which may be the chosen spot.
7 No toad spy you,
8 Hovering bird of prey pass by you;
9 Spin and die,
10 To live again a butterfly.

www.photos.com

1   The caterpillar is described as all of the following EXCEPT—

A fuzzy.
B moving quickly.
C trying to find a safe spot.
D being eaten by a bird.

2   Read the following line from the poem.

Take your walk

Which of the following lines has the same rhythm as the line above?

A *Or what not,*
B *To the shady leaf, or stalk,*
C *To live again a butterfly.*
D *Spin and die,*

3 Based upon what you know about caterpillars, explain the meaning of the last two lines from the poem. Support your answer with details from the text. (3 points)

_____

_____

_____

_____

Directions: Read the following passage and then answer the questions that follow.

Sam's Saturday
Act I, Scene 1

TIME: *A Saturday morning in late fall*

SETTING: *A front yard with a picket fence around it*

MR. THOMAS *and his grandson*, SAM, *are raking leaves.*

SAM: Gramps! Do you know what time it is?

MR. THOMAS: Oh, I'd say about ten-thirty or so.

SAM: Hey! How about this idea? I think I have some extra time after school next Tuesday. What if I rake then instead of now? I think it would be a much better time because the leaves will be a little drier and maybe it'll be warmer and . . .

MR. THOMAS: Tuesday? Well . . . I don't know. (*He stops to look up at the sky.*) The forecast calls for snow early next week. Besides, you know it gets dark just an hour or so after school's out. I'm not sure we can get it done then. I'm sorry, Sam, but I've just got to get these raked as soon as possible or . . .

SAM: You're right. Never mind. Don't worry, Gramps. We'll get it done.

He starts to rake furiously. WES, *his friend, enters, walking along on the sidewalk. He's holding a football.*

WES: Hey, Sam. What's up?

SAM: (*dropping the rake and walking over to the fence*) Not much. Well, I mean, I've got to help my grandpa rake a few leaves. But I should be done soon.

WES: Are you sure? Man! It looks like it'll take you all day!

SAM: Naw. It's really no problem.

WES: Listen, you *have* to make it to the game this afternoon. We really need you. Shawn is sick, and we'll have to forfeit without another player.

SAM: I know; I know. I'll make it. Somehow.

WES: Great. See you later!

WES *walks away, tossing the football into the air.* SAM *resumes raking.*

MR. THOMAS: Hey, Sam. Come over here a second. How are those arms doin'?

SAM: Arms? Well, actually, they're starting to feel kind of sore. I just hope I'll be able to throw a football again.

MR. THOMAS: Hope? Why Sam, your arms should be stronger after this, not weaker!

SAM: (*laughing*) That's really hard to believe, Grampa. You must be pulling my leg.

MR. THOMAS: Would I joke around with you? My doctor tells me I should do as much yard work as I can. It's the best medicine for weak muscles.

SAM: Really?

MR. THOMAS: Sure! When I was kid, I did this kind of stuff all the time, just to keep in shape. All that hard work made me as strong as an ox. I would get all my friends to help me, too.

SAM: No way! How did you do that?

MR. THOMAS: I would tell them how much fun it was! And what great skill it took to do it right. And how their arms would just bulge with muscles afterwards.

SAM: And that worked? I mean, your friends all helped you then?

MR. THOMAS: Most of the time. (*He looks up at the sky again.*) But that was long ago.

After a moment, SAM *walks back to the fence. He looks to see if* WES *is still in view.*

4   Explain when and where the play takes place. Where did you find this information?
(3 points)

_____

_____

_____

_____

5   When Sam says, "You must be pulling my leg," he means—

  A his grandfather is making him work too hard.

  B his grandfather is pulling on his leg.

  C his grandfather is teasing him.

  D his legs hurt from raking leaves.

6 Study the following line from the play.

All that hard work made me as strong as an ox.

Grandfather is really saying that—

A he was big and strong like an ox.
B he smelled like an ox after working all day.
C he looked like an ox when he was younger.
D he had a pet ox when he was a boy.

Directions: Answer the following questions about both the poem and the drama.

7 "The Caterpillar" contains all of the following EXCEPT—

A rhyme.
B meter.
C dialogue.
D descriptive words.

8 "Sam's Saturday" contains all of the following EXCEPT—

A characters.
B stage directions.
C rhyme.
D dialogue.

Points Earned/Total = _____/12

Point of View and Illustrations

Review the Standards (RL.4.6, RL.4.7)

- Compare and contrast **first-person** and **third-person points of view**
- Make **connections** between the text and the visual presentation of the text

Q: What are **first-person** and **third-person point of view**?

A: Point of view has to do with who is telling the story, or the narrator of a story or poem.

Point of view	Pronouns used	Example
First-person—A person in the story is describing the action.	*I, me, we, us, our*	The first time I rode a bike, I almost caused a three-car accident.
Third-person—An outside narrator is telling the story.	*They, them, she, he*	The three little kittens didn't obey their mama. They wandered deep into the woods and got lost.

Q: How can pictures and illustrations help me understand a story or text?

A: The pictures with a text should help you better understand the characters and the setting of the story. As you read the story, connect the illustrations with what you are reading.

 Try It

Directions: Read the following passage. Then answer the questions that follow.

Math Dance

So there I was, last Tuesday at 10:45. Mr. Cole had just given us a surprise quiz to finish in the last 15 minutes of class. Math was not my best subject, so I was ready to get the quiz over with. *Hmmm,* I thought to myself. *If a train travels west at 60 miles an hour, how long would it take to reach a town 72 miles away?*

Suddenly, I jumped out of my seat like a jack-in-the-box. I grabbed my head and danced about, laughing like a hyena. I was out of control.

"Edwin Hong, that's enough clowning around. Go straight to the office, young man!" Mr. Cole said.

I didn't wait for him to tell me a second time, as I usually did. I jumped and twirled out of the classroom. I laughed my way down the hall to the office. As I reached for the office door, the school nurse came out.

"Mrs. Garcia, help me!" I cried, still laughing and jumping.

"What is it, Edwin? Come into my office."

Inside the nurse's office, tears of laughter ran down my cheeks as I explained. "I can't help it, Mrs. Garcia. It just tickles so much! It's inside my head, here on the left side! Ha-ha-ha-ha!"

Mrs. Garcia shined a light into my ear. At first, she didn't see anything but my ear. Then, a tiny beetle came crawling out toward the light.

"It looks like this little fellow lost his way," Mrs. Garcia giggled. Now it was her turn to enjoy a good laugh. "I've seen a lot of things in all my years of nursing. But I've never seen this before! You'll be all right. You can go back to class now."

Just then, the 11:00 bell rang. I breathed a sigh of relief.

GO ON

1 The story is written from whose point of view?

   A Edwin's

   B Mr. Cole's

   C Mrs. Garcia's

   D the principal's

2 Is the story written in first-person or third-person point of view? Support your answer with details from the text. (3 points)

_____

_____

_____

_____

_____

_____

3 Which of the following details from the story does the illustration show?

   A *Mrs. Garcia shined a light into my ear.*

   B *I laughed my way down the hall to the office.*

   C *Then, a tiny beetle came crawling out toward the light.*

   D *Mrs. Garcia giggled.*

For **Examples 1 and 2**, you must think about who is telling the story. As you read, you realize that a character in the story is narrating the action. Later, you find out that the character's name is Edwin Hong. The correct answer to **Example 1** is **choice A**.

Example 2 asks you to explain whether the story is written in **first-person** or **third-person point of view.** The narrator is a character in the story; he uses the pronouns *I* and *us*. You should include these details from the text in your answer.

Good: *The story is written in first-person point of view. Edwin Hong is narrating the events that happened to him. He uses first-person pronouns such as* I *and* us.

A poor answer will not correctly identify the point of view and will not include details from the story.

Poor: *The story is written in third-person point of view.*

Example 3 asks you to make a **connection** between the illustration and the text. You should read the answer choices and decide which detail the illustration shows. The correct answer is **choice B**, *I laughed my way down the hall to the office.*

4 Read the following passage.

I was just minding my own business, trying to get home to the wife and kid beetles when all of a sudden everything went dark. It was like I was in a tunnel, but with no light at the end of it. It was pitch black. I couldn't fly my way out so I started crawling around and around, up and down.

The passage is written in—

A first person.

B second person.

C third person.

D none of the above.

5 Who is narrating the action in the passage above?

A Edwin

B Mr. Cole

C the nurse

D the beetle

6 Why does the illustration have Edwin holding a pencil in one hand and his left ear in the other? Support your answer with details from the text. (3 points)

_____

_____

_____

_____

_____

_____

_____

_____

_____

Comparing and Contrasting Stories

Review the Standard (RL.4.9)
• **Compare** and **contrast** stories from different cultures

Q: How do I **compare** and **contrast** stories from different cultures?

A: To **compare** means to show how something is the same. To **contrast** means to show how something is different. The following diagram is called a Venn diagram. It can help you compare and contrast stories.

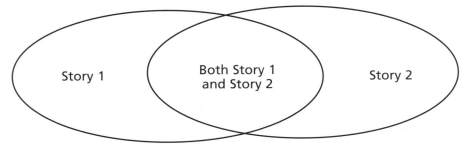

Story 1   Both Story 1 and Story 2   Story 2

When comparing and contrasting stories, consider the following:
• events
• characters
• main ideas, or themes
• morals or lessons learned
• things from nature that are explained (how we got fire, why we have seasons)

 Try It

Directions: Read the following stories. Then answer the questions that follow.

The Fox and the Crow

One day Fox saw Crow fly off with a piece of cheese in its beak and settle on a branch of a tree. "I want that cheese," said Master Fox to himself, and he walked up to the foot of the tree.

"Good day, Mistress Crow," he cried. "How well you are looking today. Your feathers are so glossy! Your eyes are so bright! I feel sure your voice must be more beautiful than any of the other birds. Please let me hear just one song from your throat. Then I will call you Queen of the Birds!"

Crow lifted up her head and began to caw her best, but the moment she opened her mouth the piece of cheese fell to the ground, only to be snapped up by Master Fox.

"That will do," said he. "That was all I wanted. In exchange for your cheese I will give you a piece of advice for the future. Never trust someone who gives you too many compliments."

Brer Rabbit, Brer Bear, and the Farm

Brer Rabbit and his friend Brer Bear decided what they wanted more than anything was to be farmers.

Now Brer Bear was lucky to find himself a big ole farm with soil richer and darker than he'd ever seen. When he sniffed that soil along with the sweet air, he swore he could smell ripe vegetables and fruits. And this was before he'd even planted any! He danced when he thought of all the tasty crops he could grow. With his big bear claws he tore down the old house on his land and got busy building himself a new one. Singin' and whistlin' and a'tap-tap-tapping was all you could hear around Brer Bear's farm.

But all Brer Rabbit could find was a small patch of very poor ground, with no house on it at all.

Brer Rabbit, though, was very proud. He certainly did not want to admit to Brer Bear that his land was poor. Instead, he went to his friend and said, "I'm fixin' to make my farm even bigger. Perhaps you'd like to rent me some of your land to go with my own."

Brer Bear, of course, knew Brer Rabbit's land was awful, so he made this deal. He told Brer Rabbit he could use his land for free, as long as he did all the work himself. Then when his crop was ready, he had to share it with Brer Bear.

This didn't sound like too good a deal, Brer Rabbit thought. So he asked, "But how will we divide the crop fairly between us?"

"A-ha," thought Brer Bear, "I can really outsmart that Rabbit this time." He answered, "I'll take all the tops of your crop, and you can have all the bottoms."

Brer Rabbit agreed. Then he thought and thought about what to plant. When he decided, he picked up his tools and worked and weeded all through the hot summer. Finally, at harvesttime, he called Brer Bear over. "Come and take the tops of the crop, please," he said.

Brer Bear came right over, but he found that Brer Rabbit had planted potatoes! All Brer Bear got was the useless, leafy tops. But it was his own fault for trying to outsmart Brer Rabbit.

1 How are the characters of Brer Rabbit and Master Fox similar? Support your answer with details from the stories. (5 points)

_____

_____

_____

_____

_____

_____

_____

_____

_____

_____

_____

Example 1 asks you to **compare**, or show similarities, between Brer Rabbit and Master Fox. Brer Rabbit and Fox are both smart and tricky. They see something they want and they figure out a way to get it. A good answer will include details from the stories.

Good: *Brer Rabbit and Master Fox are similar because they are sneaky and tricky. Brer Bear says that Brer Rabbit can use his farmland, but Rabbit has to give Bear all of the tops of the plants he grows. So Brer Rabbit plants potatoes that grow underground. Fox outsmarts Crow by telling her how wonderful she is and then asking her to sing for him. The cheese falls out of her mouth, and then Fox eats it.*

A poor answer will not show important similarities and will not contain specific details from the story.

Poor: *Both Brer Rabbit and Master Fox are animals who want food. And they get it from Brer Bear and Crow.*

2 What lessons are learned by Brer Bear and Crow? Are they similar in any way? Support your answer with details from the text. (3 points)

_____

_____

_____

_____

_____

_____

_____

_____

_____

Test-Taking Tips

1 Point of view refers to who is telling the story. First-person point of view uses the pronouns _I_, _we_, _us_, and _our_. One of the characters in the story is describing the events. Third-person point of view is used when an outside narrator is telling the story.

2 To make connections between the text and illustrations, ask yourself, _Which part of the story does the picture show? How does the picture help me understand the story?_

3 When comparing and contrasting two stories, think about how the characters, events, and lessons learned in the story are similar or different.

Go for it!

Unit Three Practice Test

Estimated time: 20 minutes

Directions: Read the passage. Then answer the questions that follow.

Crow Brings Daylight

Once known as Eskimos, the Inuit people live in the Arctic regions of far northern Alaska and Canada.

Listen, children, as I tell you a story of long, long ago, when the world was still new. Then the Inuit lived in darkness all year long. They could not hunt as far as they do now. They could not see the polar bear before he attacked. But because I, Crow, was gifted with flight and could travel back and forth between the northlands and the South, I explained light to the people. Soon they were captivated by the story of daylight that these southern people enjoyed. The yearning for daylight was so strong that they begged me to bring it to them. At first I refused, but the people pled with me until finally I agreed to make the long journey to the South.

I flew for many miles through the endless dark of the North. I grew weary many times and almost turned back. Suddenly, the daylight world burst upon me with all its glory and brilliance. When my eyes had adjusted to the brightness, I saw a village beside a wide river. As I watched, a beautiful girl came and dipped a large bucket into the icy waters of the river. Then I turned myself into a tiny speck of dust, drifted down, and settled into the girl's fur cloak.

The girl returned to her village and entered a warm lodge. I looked around and spotted a box that glowed around the edges. Daylight, I thought. On the floor, a little boy was playing. I floated into the ear of the little boy and scratched him. Immediately the child sat up and rubbed at his ear. He started to cry, and his grandfather, the village chief, came to see what was wrong.

"Why are you crying?" the chief asked, kneeling beside the child.

Inside the little boy's ear, I whispered: "You want to play with a ball of daylight." The little boy rubbed at his ear and then repeated my words.

As I watched, the chief removed a glowing ball from the box in the corner, tied it with a string, and gave it to the little boy. The child laughed happily, tugging at the string and watching the ball bounce.

www.photos.com

Then I scratched the inside of the boy's ear again. When the boy cried, I whispered: "You want to go outside to play." The boy rubbed at his ear and then repeated my words to his grandfather. Immediately, the chief lifted up the small child and carried him outside.

www.istockphotos.com

As soon as we were outside, I swooped out of the child's ear and changed back to my natural form. I darted toward the ball of light and grabbed the string with my claws. Up I rose into the endless blue sky with the ball of light trailing along behind me.

Away I flew into the North. As I flew, daylight broke through the dark with dazzling brilliance. When I reached the Inuit village, the people all gazed up at me in amazement. Swooping down, I dropped the ball, and it shattered upon the ground. Daylight burst outward, illuminating every dark place and chasing away every shadow. The sky grew bright and turned blue, and the snow sparkled so brightly that the people had to shade their eyes.

The Inuit cried out with joy, but I told them that the daylight would not last forever. Because I had only stolen one ball of daylight, the light would not last all year. The light would need to rest for six months every year to regain its strength. During that six-month period, the darkness would return and there would be only a few hours of daylight.

However, the people were so happy they thanked me over and over again. To this day, the winter months are dark and cold and the summer months are lighter and warmer. And they are always kind to my ancestors, since it was I, Crow, who first brought them the light.

1　The pictures included with the story help you understand all of the following EXCEPT—

  A what a crow looks like.

  B where the Inuit people live.

  C what the Inuit people look like.

  D why the Inuit people need daylight.

2　The story is told—

  A by one of the Inuit who asks Crow to get daylight.

  B by an Inuit narrator.

  C by the crow who brings the daylight.

  D by the child with the ball of daylight.

GO ON

Directions: Read the following passage. Then answer the questions that follow.

How Coyote Stole Fire

Long ago, fire was a secret guarded by the Fire Beings. Men and women did not have fire. In the long cold winters, old people shivered in their teepees. Babies cried in their mothers' arms. There was no relief from the cold. Each spring, the great warriors would mourn for those who had died of the cold in the winter.

Coyote watched the people from the edges of their villages. He peeked inside their teepees and listened to their talk. He saw their sorrow when the cold caused deaths.

"I know what these people need," said Coyote to himself. "They need a piece of the warm sun to keep inside their teepees. They need a piece of the sun that gives warmth all winter long. They need fire."

©Corel

Coyote knew where to find fire. On top of a certain mountain, the Fire Beings lived. These Beings selfishly guarded the secret of fire for themselves. Coyote decided to teach the Fire Beings a lesson by stealing their fire for humankind.

When darkness fell, Coyote crept up the mountain. At the top, he crouched at the edge of the clearing. There, the three Fire Beings sat before a blazing fire. During the night, the Fire Beings took turns sleeping inside their teepee. Two slept while one guarded the fire.

Coyote saw their weakness. When the one guard went into the teepee to sleep, the sleeping guard took several minutes to come outside. Before leaving the teepee, the Being stretched and yawned and took slow, sleepy steps.

Coyote waited for one of these times. He watched the guard go inside the teepee. He listened for the next guard to begin yawning and shuffling inside the teepee.

Then Coyote sprang at the fire. He grabbed a branch that burned on one end. With this torch, he raced down the mountain. Behind him he heard the howl of the Fire Beings. They realized they had been robbed of the secret of fire.

Coyote gave the fire to humankind, who guards it well. At night, Coyote still crouches in the darkness and gazes at the light. He laughs quietly to himself about how he stole fire.

3 The story is written—

A in first person.

B in third person.

C by the Coyote.

D by the Fire Beings.

Directions: Use the Venn diagram and both stories to help you answer the following questions.

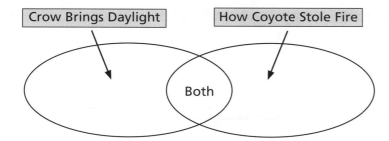

4 Which of the following would fit under **Crow Brings Daylight**?

  A told in third-person
  B told in first-person
  C told by a narrator
  D told by the coyote

5 Which of the following would fit under **How Coyote Stole Fire**?

  A Men and women begged Coyote to steal the fire.
  B Coyote goes to the South to steal the fire.
  C Coyote wants to teach the Fire Beings a lesson by stealing the fire.
  D Coyote becomes a speck of dust and sneaks into a teepee.

6 Explain three ways that Crow and Coyote are similar. Think about what the characters do and how they act. Be sure to include details from the stories in your answer. (5 points).

_____

_____

_____

_____

_____

_____

_____

_____

Points Earned/Total = _____/10

Reading Informational Text Lesson 9

Explain and Infer

Review the Standard (RI.4.1, W.4.9)

- Refer to details in a text
- Draw **inferences** from a text

Q: Why should I refer to the text when explaining what it says or when making an **inference**?

A: When writing or talking about something you read, you should always refer to the text. By supporting your ideas with details and examples from the text, you will be sure your answers are accurate. Compare the following sentences.

Poor: *The article explains that flossing your teeth is important.*

Good: *In the second paragraph, the article explains that flossing removes food in between the teeth where a toothbrush can't reach.*

The second sentence is much better because it refers to specific details from the text.

Q: How do I make an **inference** from a nonfiction text?

A: An **inference** is an educated guess. To make an inference, you must think about what the text says and what you already know. Suppose you read the following sentence:

Flossing only helps if you do it right. The plaque stays on your teeth if you don't wrap the floss around the tooth and use a sawing motion.

After reading this sentence, you understand that flossing can be done incorrectly. You already know that if you don't take care of your teeth, you can get cavities. Thus, you can infer that someone could floss every day and still get cavities if they don't floss the correct way.

 Try It

Directions: Read the following passage. Then answer the questions that follow.

1   Don't you just love to sweat? Well, you should. When our bodies sweat as a result of physical activity, wonderful things happen. The simple definition of sweat is that it is salty water that is produced when we get hot. When we sweat, this water on our skin helps cool us down. But sweat does so much more than that!

2   Sweating has been considered so important that it was even discussed in the oldest known medical document. Even then, people knew that sweating was as important to our health as eating and sleeping. As we begin to play a game of soccer or climb a tree, our muscles go to work. They flex and push, making our bodies warm up. Before we know it, our bodies are producing sweat.

3   This is great news! Sweat flushes out toxic metals that are absorbed into our bodies. With pollution in the air and toxins in our water, metals such as copper, zinc, and mercury are absorbed into the body. But sweat flushes all of that out, cleaning our bodies from the inside out. Eating too many french fries and cheeseburgers may also be toxic, putting too much salt into our systems. By sweating, those unwanted wastes are removed too.

4   Sweat also helps our bodies heal. Have you ever played so hard your muscles were sore the next day? This is because a liquid called *lactic acid* has built up inside the muscles, causing them to be stiff and sore. We might think the worst thing we could do would be to play hard and make those muscles tired all over again. In truth, physical activity is the best thing we can do. By moving and sweating, the lactic acid is washed out, making us feel stronger and refreshed.

5   Finally, sweating is great for our skin. Sweating from physical activity cleanses the body by opening the pores of our skin. Blood rushes to the skin for a healthier look. It is also true that when we sweat, our bodies crave more water. Water helps cleanse our bodies, getting rid of toxins. So the next time someone tells you, "Don't sweat it," say, "But I want to!"

---

1   Which of the following details supports the idea that sweat cleans out the toxic metals in our bodies?

    A We sweat when we get hot.

    B Sweating opens the pores of the skin.

    C Sweat cools our bodies down.

    D Sweat flushes out copper, zinc, and mercury.

2   Read the following sentence from paragraph 2.

Sweating has been considered so important that it was even discussed in the oldest known medical document. Even then, people knew that sweating was as important to our health as eating and sleeping.

Based upon this passage, we can infer that—

    A people today don't think eating and sleeping are important.

    B no one studied medicine in ancient times.

    C sweating is more important than eating and sleeping.

    D people from ancient times studied and wrote about health.

3 How does sweating help the body get rid of toxins from food? Refer to specific details from the text in your answer. (3 points)

_____

_____

_____

_____

_____

For **Example 1**, you must find a detail from the passage that supports the idea that sweat cleans out toxic metals from our bodies. By closely reading paragraph 3, you find the detail that sweat flushes out copper, zinc, and mercury that are absorbed into our bodies. Thus the correct answer is **choice D**.

Example 2 asks you to make an **inference** based upon a passage from paragraph 2. Remember an inference is an educated guess based upon the text. You can eliminate choices A and C because the text says that "sweating was as important to our health as eating and sleeping." Choice B isn't a good inference because the text refers to old medical documents, so people were studying medicine. The best answer is **choice D**.

For **Example 3**, you must refer to the text as you answer a question. A good answer will include specific details.

Good: _Sweating helps the body get rid of toxins from foods that contain salt and other toxins. In paragraph 3, the writer explains how sweating removes toxins such as salt from our bodies._

A poor answer will not refer to details from the text.

Poor: _Sweating removes salt from our bodies._

◎ Try It On Your Own

4 How does sweat help our bodies heal? Refer to details from the text to support your answer. (3 points)

_____

_____

_____

_____

_____

5 Based upon paragraph 5, we can infer that—

A sweating causes pimples and skin problems.

B the pores on our skin are smaller when we are not sweating.

C we shouldn't drink water when we sweat.

D we should not take a shower after sweating.

Main Ideas and Supporting Details

Review the Standards (RI.4.2, RI.4.3)

- Determine the **main idea** and **key details** of a text
- **Summarize** the text

Q: How do I determine the **main idea** and supporting **key details** of a text?

A: The **main idea** of a text is the central thing the passage is about. After reading a passage, you should be able to state the main idea in a short sentence. **Key details** are the ideas that support the main idea. Sometimes using a web can help you think about the main idea and important supporting details.

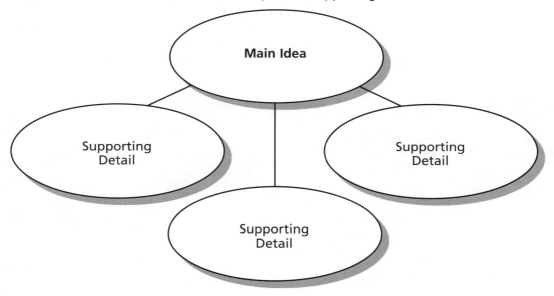

Q: How do I write a **summary**?

A: A **summary** is a short written explanation of the main idea and the key supporting details of a passage. The first sentence of your summary should state the main idea of the pasage. The rest of the sentences should describe the supporting details. A summary should always be shorter than the passage you are summarizing.

GO ON

Directions: Read the following passage. Then answer the questions that follow.

Many wild birds depend on people to feed them. This is especially true in places where many houses and roads have been built. When people build, they take over open land where birds look for food. Then if people don't provide food for them, the birds must find a new place to live.

There are many ways to feed birds. One way is to put up bird feeders filled with seed. Blackbirds and cardinals like to eat from feeders. Other birds, such as sparrows, like to eat seeds that are scattered on the ground. Robins enjoy eating pieces of apples and oranges. Planting fruit trees is an even better way to attract birds that have a sweet tooth. If your yard has an oak tree, crows and woodpeckers may pay you a visit. They love to crack and eat the acorns from the trees. A simple flower garden will attract the beautiful hummingbird, which is drawn to the bright colors of the flowers.

If you are interested in feeding your wild feathered friends, you can try some of these ideas. Don't worry if you don't see any birds at first. It may take awhile for them to find the food. Once they find it, though, they'll keep coming back for more, and they will tell all their friends.

www.photos.com

1 What is the main idea of the first paragraph?

   A People destroy the homes of wild birds so they will leave.

   B People may need to feed wild birds when the birds' homes have been destroyed.

   C Wild birds are starving because no one cares about them.

   D Everyone should have a bird feeder.

2   Which detail BEST completes the web below?

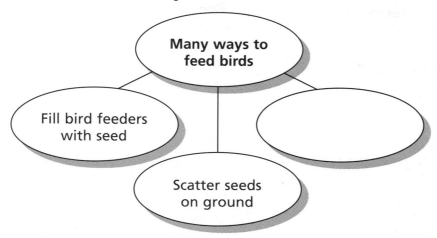

  A Birds depend on people
  B Find new places to live
  C Tell all their friends
  D Give pieces of apples and oranges

3   What is an important detail about hummingbirds?

  A They like oak trees.
  B They eat oranges.
  C They are drawn to brightly colored flowers.
  D They like to crack and eat acorns.

4   Write a summary of the passage. Be sure to include the main idea and all the important supporting details. (3 points)

_____

_____

_____

_____

_____

_____

   Example 1 asks you what the **main idea** of the first paragraph is. The main idea of a paragraph or passage is the main thing that the writer wants you to know about the topic. Although the author doesn't directly state the main idea in the first paragraph, you can infer that the best answer is **choice B**.
   Making a web like the one in **Example 2** may help you figure out the main idea and **supporting details** of a passage. Supporting details give information or facts about the

main idea. In this example, you are to choose the detail that supports the main idea that there are many ways to feed birds. Choices A, B, and C are details about birds, but they do not support the idea at the center of the web. Only choice D states a way to feed birds. **Choice D** is correct.

Example 3 is another question about supporting details. According to the passage, the only detail that relates to hummingbirds is choice C, *They are drawn to brightly colored flowers*. **Choice C** is correct.

Example 4 asks you to write a **summary** of the passage. A good summary contains the main idea and key supporting details.

Good: *It is important for people to feed wild birds. This can be done by putting out feed in feeders or on the ground and by planting fruit trees or flower gardens. If you are patient, many birds will come to eat in your yard.*

A poor response will not include the main idea or key supporting details.

Poor: *Birds like to eat different things. Hummingbirds love bright colors, but robins like apples and oranges.*

◎ Try It On Your Own

Directions: Read the following passage. Then answer the questions that follow.

Kids at a Florida elementary school found out that the buddy system can work wonders—for both kids and plants. When an old trailer was removed from their school grounds, it left behind an ugly patch of ground. But two teachers looked at that patch of ground and had an idea. Why not make it into a garden?

Most of their students lived in apartments and had never planted anything before. The teachers thought this would be a good time for them to learn where vegetables come from. They came up with a plan, and they wanted fourth grade students to take the lead.

Each fourth grade student worked with a few kindergarten "buddies." The teams, with the fourth graders in charge, had to research gardens and vegetable plants. They used fiction and nonfiction books, magazines, and the Internet. Each team came up with a plan. They drew diagrams of their garden. Then each team presented their plan to the rest of the class. The class discussed the plans, decided what would work best, and voted on one final plan.

The kids had learned through research that some plants grow better next to certain "buddy" plants. For example, lettuce often withers and dies without protection from the hot sun. But tall bean plants, when planted nearby, can shade the lettuce. In the same way, pea plants can shade the tender seedlings of watermelons. And bugs naturally stay away from marigold flowers, so the students planted marigolds near the tomatoes. This kept the tomatoes nearly pest-free.

The partners also learned that growing a variety of vegetables can help keep the soil healthy. When one plant uses up a nutrient in the soil, another plant can replace it. For example, as corn grows it uses up a lot of a nutrient called *nitrogen*. But peas and beans planted later in the same spot can add nitrogen back into the soil.

The teams worked hard. They cleaned the ground, prepared the soil, planted the seeds, and kept everything moist. They followed a planting calendar to make sure they planted seeds at the proper time.

When the garden was all planted, the fourth graders had learned something else: how to be leaders. "They took their jobs very seriously," their teacher said. "They helped their young buddies and kept them on track."

---

5 Which of the following details does NOT belong in a summary of this passage?

   A Each fourth grader worked with a few kindergarten "buddies."

   B They used fiction and nonfiction books to do research.

   C The class learned that some plants grow better next to "buddy" plants.

   D The fourth graders learned how to be leaders.

6 Which of the following details supports the idea that growing a variety of vegetables keeps the soil healthy?

   A Most students had never planted anything before.

   B Tall bean plants shade sun-sensitive lettuce plants.

   C Each team came up with a plan for the garden.

   D Peas and bean plants put nitrogen back into the ground.

7 Summarize the passage in your own words. Be sure to include the main idea and key details from the passage. (3 points)

_____

_____

_____

_____

_____

_____

Test-Taking Tips

1 Sometimes the main idea is stated directly in the passage, and other times it is implied. Look for a sentence that summarizes the main idea. If you can't find one that makes sense, you may have to state the main idea in your own words.

2 If the main idea is stated, it may not be the first sentence of a paragraph. If the first sentence is not what the paragraph is mostly about, look at the other sentences.

3 When looking for relevant details, make sure the detail relates to the main idea.

4 When writing a summary, include the main idea of the entire passage in the first sentence of the summary. The rest of the sentences should include key supporting details. Do not include minor details.

Go for it!

Unit Four Practice Test

Estimated time: 25 minutes

Directions: Read the following passage. Then answer the questions that follow.

Helping Stranded Sea Animals

1   The New England Aquarium is a kind of zoo for ocean animals. Besides being a home for the animals, the aquarium has exhibits and programs about ocean life. One of the most important things the aquarium staff does is to care for hurt or lost ocean animals. For example, several times they have helped rescue stranded whales. A sea animal is stranded when it goes on shore by mistake. It may be alone, or it may have many other animals with it.

www.photos.com

2   One morning in 1986, an aquarium worker named Greg Early received some bad news. About 40 whales were stranded on a Massachusetts beach.

3   Greg went to see what could be done for the whales. Healthy adult whales were guided back to the deep ocean waters. Many workers helped with this job. Hurt or sick whales had to be put to sleep. Three young whales were a special problem. They had been separated from their mothers and were too young to care for themselves in the ocean. Greg decided to bring the young ones back to the aquarium.

4   For six months, Greg and his crew watched over the young whales at the aquarium's Animal Care Center. When the whales were healthy and strong, it was time to return them to the ocean. Would the whales become frightened or lost when they were released? Greg decided to put radio tags on the whales to keep track of them in the ocean. The radio signals would let the crew know if the whales were in trouble.

5   The young whales were taken to a part of the ocean where a group of whales had been spotted. When they were released, the three young whales swam away and joined the group.

6   Four years later, in 1990, another large group of whales was stranded not too far from the aquarium. This group included 55 whales, and aquarium workers did what they could to help. Two young females were brought to the Animal Care Center. After they were nursed back to health, they too were released into the ocean.

7   Whales are stranded most often in December, when the weather is bad. No one is sure, but it may be that the weather drives the animals to shore. However, whale strandings can occur at any time. In 2000, a group of 11 whales was found stranded on the Fourth of July, in fine weather. None of the whales seemed to be ill either.

8   Whatever the time of year, the New England Aquarium's rescue team is ready to help stranded animals. After all, this important job must be done, good weather or bad.

1 Which supporting detail from paragraph 3 BEST completes the web below?

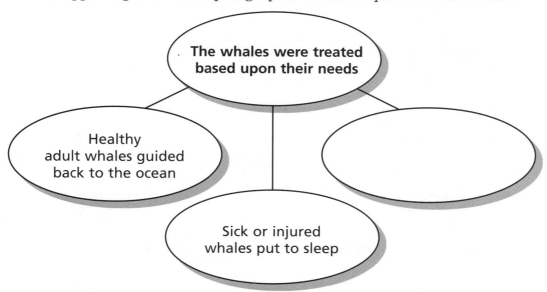

A Some whales were young

B Greg Early tried to help the whales

C Three young whales brought back to aquarium

D Many workers helped relocate healthy adult whales

2 This article is mainly about—

A the New England Aquarium rescuing stranded whales.

B why Greg Early likes being a rescue worker.

C the kinds of exhibits that the New England Aquarium has.

D why sea animals get stranded.

3 What is paragraph 7 of this article mainly about?

A when whale strandings often happen

B 11 whales that were stranded in 2000

C the bad weather in New England in December

D some stranded whales that are ill

4 Based on the information in paragraph 1, the reader can infer that the New England Aquarium—

A relies on volunteers to do the work.

B teaches people about ocean animals.

C captures ocean animals from the wild and puts them on exhibit.

D is the only whale rescue group working in the United States.

GO ON

5 Describe what happened to the three young whales that were stranded without their mothers. Refer to details from the text in your answer. (3 points)

_____

_____

_____

_____

_____

_____

_____

6 Write a summary of the passage. (3 points)

_____

_____

_____

_____

_____

_____

_____

_____

_____

_____

_____

Points Earned/Total = _____/10

Reading Informational Text Lesson 11

Text Structures

Review the Standards (RI.4.3, RI.4.5)
- Explain the ideas in nonfiction texts
- Describe the **structure** of a text

Q: How will understanding purpose help me understand informational texts?

A: As you read a text ask yourself, *Why is the author writing this?* This will help you understand the writer's purpose. The writer may want to inform, to explain, to describe, or to persuade.

Q: How will understanding text **structures** help me become a better reader?

A: Understanding the **structure** of a passage, or how the ideas are arranged, will help you understand how ideas fit together.

Structure	Look for these key words
Chronological (Order of Events)	*first, next, then, later, after, in 1965*
Comparison/Contrast	*on the other hand, different from, but, however, likewise, in the same way*
Cause/Effect	*causes, influences, as a result, because of, a reason for*
Problem/Solution	*problem, solution, solved, reason*

GO ON

Directions: Read the following passage. Then answer the questions that follow.

The Woman Who Studied the Sky

In the early 1800s, when Maria Mitchell was born, young women were expected to marry and have children. Maria had different ideas, though. Like many girls, Maria went to school to learn to read and write. But she also became very interested in math and science. She studied these subjects so eagerly that, when she was 17, she opened up her own school. Maria's father encouraged her interests. He taught her how to use his telescope to look at the stars and planets. Before long, Maria fell in love with the science of astronomy.

After Maria's school closed, she worked in a library. But every night she studied the sky through her telescope. One night in 1847, Maria saw a "star" where she had not seen one before. She looked the next night, and the "star's" position had changed. Maria realized that she had spotted a comet. This discovery made her famous. The king of Denmark gave her a gold medal. In the following year, Maria was elected the first woman member of the American Academy of Arts and Sciences.

In 1865, not long after Vassar College opened, Maria was asked to be a teacher there. The school had a large telescope, which both Maria and her students used. As a teacher at Vassar, Maria continued her research. She studied the surfaces of Saturn and Jupiter, and in 1878 traveled 2000 miles to Colorado to witness an eclipse.

1 The purpose of this passage is to—

   A describe the history of Vassar College.

   B describe Maria Mitchell's childhood.

   C explain how Maria Mitchell discovered a comet.

   D describe Maria Mitchell's discoveries in astronomy.

2 The overall structure used in this text is—

  A chronological order.

  B problem/solution.

  C cause/effect.

  D comparison.

3 According to the passage, which event in Maria's life happened first?

  A Maria became a teacher at Vassar.

  B Maria was elected to the American Academy of Arts and Sciences.

  C Maria opened her own school.

  D Maria worked in a library.

4 Study the chart below.

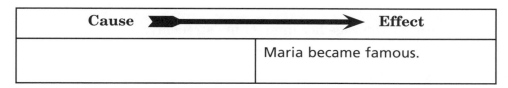

Cause	→	Effect
		Maria became famous.

Which of the following belongs under "Cause"?

  A Maria fell in love with astronomy.

  B Maria studied the surfaces of Saturn and Jupiter.

  C Maria opened up her own school.

  D In 1847, Maria discovered a comet.

For **Example 1**, you must think about the **purpose** of the passage, or why the passage was written. Think about the title and the details the writer includes in the passage. The passage explains important events in Maria's life. Although choices A, B, and C contain ideas found in the passage, none of them explains why the entire passage was written. Only choice D gives the purpose of the entire passage. The correct answer is **choice D**.

Example 2 asks you to think about **text structure**, or how the ideas in the text are arranged. Notice the key words used to show how the events are related: *In the early 1800s, Before long, After Maria's school closed*. These words show that the passage is in time order, or chronological order. The correct answer is **choice A**.

In **Example 3**, you are asked to identify which event in Maria's life happened first. According to the passage, Maria opened her own school before she worked in a library, was elected to the American Academy of Arts and Sciences, or became a teacher at Vassar. **Choice C** is correct.

Example 4 asks you to think about a cause and effect found in the passage. You must decide what caused Maria to become famous. According to the passage, it was because she discovered a comet. Maria's discovering a comet was the cause, and Maria's becoming famous was the effect. **Choice D** is correct.

5 According to the first paragraph, how was Maria different from other girls?

   A She learned to read and write.

   B She was expected to marry and have children.

   C She studied math and science.

   D She became a teacher.

6 Why did Maria travel to Colorado in 1878?

   A She went to teach at a different college.

   B She was studying a new comet.

   C She was studying the surfaces of Saturn and Jupiter.

   D She was witnessing an eclipse.

7 How did Maria's father encourage her interest in astronomy?

   A He taught her to read and write.

   B He helped her open her own school.

   C He taught her how to use his telescope.

   D He found her a job in a library.

Reasons and Evidence

Review the Standard (RI.4.8)

• Explain how an author uses **reasons** and **evidence**

Q: How do writers use **reason** and **evidence**?

A: Sometimes you read a text and realize that the writer is trying to convince you to think or act a certain way. The writer states an opinion and then tries to persuade you to agree with his or her opinion by giving **reasons** and **evidence**. Reasons are statements why you should do or believe something. Evidence is facts that support reasons and may include scientific ideas or examples.

Opinion: You should eat healthy food.

Reason 1: Eating healthy food keeps you from becoming overweight.

Evidence: Kids who drink soft drinks and other sugary drinks are more likely to become obese than kids who don't.

Reason 2: Eating healthy food helps you feel better.

Evidence: Kids who eat six servings of fruits and vegetables a day are sick less often than kids who don't.

A writer may also use emotional language to try to persuade you by making you feel bad or good. However, emotional language is not as persuasive as good reasons.

Emotional language: If you eat too much junk food, you will get so fat that everyone will make fun of you!

GO ON

Try It

Directions: Read the following passage. Then answer the questions that follow.

A Home for Everyone

Dear Editor,

1 I am a student at Grayville School, and I am writing to bring up a serious issue. It has to do with the animals in our community.

2 As everyone knows, the weather is starting to get colder. Soon it will be below freezing every night, or at least most nights. It is not the kind of weather for living things to be out in!

3 Last year in our town there were plenty of animals out in the cold at night. One time our family left a basketball game at about 9:30. Huddled near the door of the gym was a little cat. It looked like it was freezing! We tried to get it to come to us, but it was so scared that it ran away. This cat did not have any collar on, so we weren't sure what to do next.

4 Other students at our school have had similar experiences. One told our class about how he and his father found a puppy one morning. It had hidden itself underneath their back porch. During the night they thought they heard some soft, moaning cries, but they couldn't figure out where the cries were coming from. They were sure it was the puppy, whimpering in the cold.

5 Where do these poor animals come from? We discussed this in school, and we think that many are animals that people don't want any longer. Maybe people were not able to keep that little freezing cat. Maybe someone's dog had puppies, and the owner couldn't give them all away. Or maybe the animals just got out by mistake and were lost.

6 What I want to say is this: You can't just throw animals away! If they are yours, or if you let them come into the world, you are responsible for them. Sometimes people's dogs or cats have puppies or kittens. If there is no good home waiting for these animals, then people shouldn't let their dogs or cats give birth to them. Take your animal to the vet and have it spayed or neutered.

7 The other thing is that you should think seriously before you ever get a pet. Are you ready for the responsibility? Are you willing to take care of your animal every day? Will you be sure it never gets out by mistake and gets lost? Unless you can answer yes to all these questions, you should never get a pet in the first place.

8 Winter is coming. Remember that cats and dogs deserve warm homes, just like people do.

Sincerely,

Maya Smith

1 The writer of the letter is trying to persuade people to—

   A build a shelter for homeless animals.
   B take care of their pets.
   C adopt a pet from a shelter.
   D put collars on their pets.

2 In paragraphs 3 and 4, the writer—

   A gives examples of animals who were cold and homeless.
   B gives reasons why someone should not get a pet.
   C describes her own pets.
   D gives reasons why pet owners should put collars on their pets.

3 In paragraph 7, what is the writer trying to persuade the readers to do? Use examples from the text to support your answer. (3 points)

_____

_____

_____

_____

_____

_____

_____

_____

_____

Example 1 asks you to think about why the writer wrote the letter. This may be a little tricky because the writer begins the letter by telling stories about pets that were abandoned in the cold. She tells these stories to get to her opinion in paragraph 6. In paragraph 6 she states, "You can't just throw animals away! If they are yours, or if you let them come into the world, you are responsible for them." **Choice B** is correct.

Example 2 asks you to identify the main idea of paragraphs 3 and 4. As mentioned before, the writer tells stories about pets found in the cold, or **choice A**.

To answer **Example 3**, you must think about what the writer is trying to persuade the readers to do in paragraph 7. Paragraph 7 is mainly trying to convince people to think about whether they are ready to take care of a pet before they buy one. A good answer will include details from the passage.

Good: *In paragraph 7, the writer is trying to persuade the readers to think about whether they are responsible enough to take care of a pet. She asks the readers to think about whether they are willing to make sure the pet doesn't get out by mistake or get lost. If not, you shouldn't get a pet.*

Poor: *The writer is trying to persuade the readers to take care of their pets.*

GO ON

Directions: Read the following passage. Then answer the questions that follow.

Every year the fourth and fifth graders put on a musical in the spring. This year the musical is *Annie*. All fourth and fifth graders should get involved in the musical.

No matter what you love to do, there is a place for you to use your abilities in the cast and crew of *Annie*. If you love to sing and dance, try out for one of the lead roles or a part in the chorus. The musical has some great songs, including "It's a Hard Knock Life" and "Tomorrow." If you enjoy art and making stuff, you can help design the set. We also need people to help with advertising and promotions. If you enjoy helping people, you can be an usher or assist backstage.

Being involved in the production is a great way to have fun with your friends after school. Why go home and be bored when you can hang out with your friends? Or you may even make some new friends. Fifth grader Edward Chang says, "Last year I did the lights for the production of *Oliver*. I made a ton of new friends." Plus you'll have a part in making this year's musical the best one ever.

Be sure to attend the informational meeting and tryouts next Tuesday and Wednesday after school in the performance center. Don't be left out!

4   The writer of this passage is trying to convince you to—

   A help backstage with a musical production.

   B have fun with your friends after school.

   C make the production of *Annie* the best one ever.

   D get involved in the school's production of *Annie*.

5   What two reasons does the writer give to support his main idea? Explain these ideas using details from the text. (3 points)

   _____

   _____

   _____

   _____

   _____

   _____

   _____

6 Which of the following details from the passage gives evidence to support the idea that being involved in the musical is a good way to have fun with your friends?

A *If you love to sing and dance, try out for one of the lead roles or a part in the chorus.*

B *Fifth grader Edward Chang says, "Last year I did the lights for the production of* Oliver. *I made a ton of new friends."*

C *Don't be left out!*

D *The musical has some great songs, including "It's a Hard Knock Life" and "Tomorrow."*

Test-Taking Tips

1 When you want to discover if a passage is organized chronologically, look for signal words such as *first, then, tomorrow,* and *afterward.* Years and people's ages can also be clues (as in *"when she was 17"*).

2 If the main idea is stated, it may not be the first sentence of a paragraph. If the first sentence is not what the paragraph is mostly about, look at the other sentences.

3 When reading a text that expresses an opinion, look for reasons and evidence the writer uses to persuade you. Emotional language appeals to your feelings.

Go for it!

Unit Five Practice Test

Estimated time: 20 minutes

Directions: Read the following passage. Then answer the questions that follow.

1   At the center of most cities in the United States, a cluster of tall buildings reach upward toward the sky. If you look up at them from the ground, they appear to touch, or scrape, the sky. How are these amazing skyscrapers built?

2   The term "skyscraper" was first used in the 1880s shortly after tall buildings were constructed in the United States. Before then the world had lots of tall towers made of stone. But these towers had thick, heavy walls and the rooms were dark and cramped.

3   Several developments caused modern builders to be able to build higher buildings. First, iron and steel were invented to give skyscrapers a strong support system. Then the elevator came along so that people didn't have to climb up many flights of stairs. As taller towers were built, architects were able to improve the design of skyscrapers to resist strong winds that rush against buildings that reach almost 1,500 feet in the air.

www.photos.com

4   Not all skyscrapers look the same, yet all skyscrapers have two main parts. What you see above the ground is called the *superstructure*. But there is also a part that you do not see. It is called the *foundation*, and it is under the ground. Both the superstructure and the foundation support the weight, or load, of a skyscraper. A skyscraper also has a steel or concrete frame to support it in the same way that bones support your body.

5   When someone wants to build a new skyscraper, an architect and an engineer work together to create a plan. Once the plan is ready, the construction crew begins its work. First, large machines dig a hole in the ground for the foundation. Sometimes the hole can be deep enough for a two-story house. A layer of rock or soil goes in the hole. Then steel or concrete columns are placed on top of that layer.

6   Next, cranes lift large pieces of the frame—the skyscraper's skeleton—and place them on top of the foundation. Construction of the superstructure has begun. A skyscraper's frame can often be completed in just a few weeks.

7   Once the frame is complete, crews begin putting on the outside walls and windows. Floors are put in place. Then systems such as air-conditioning and plumbing are installed. It can take several years to complete the entire skyscraper.

1   The purpose of the passage is to—

    A explain how skyscrapers are built.

    B describe the machines used to build skyscrapers.

    C describe the world's tallest skyscrapers.

    D explain how to become an architect.

2   Explain two of the modern developments that caused skyscrapers to be able to be built. Refer to facts in the passage in your answer. (3 points)

_____

_____

_____

_____

_____

3   All of the following facts are true of the foundation of a skyscraper EXCEPT—

    A you can't see it after the building is finished.

    B it is under the ground.

    C it supports the weight of the building.

    D it is the frame of the building.

4   The structure of paragraphs 5–7 is—

    A chronological order.

    B problem/solution.

    C cause/effect.

    D comparison/contrast.

5   Which comes first when building a skyscraper?

    A A layer of rock goes into the hole in the ground.

    B Large machines dig a hole.

    C Architects work with engineers to create a plan.

    D Steel or concrete columns are put in place.

GO ON

6 Why were the tall towers that came before skyscrapers not good for people to live and work in? Explain the reasons given in the passage. (3 points)

_____

_____

_____

_____

_____

_____

_____

_____

_____

_____

_____

_____

_____

_____

_____

_____

_____

Points Earned/Total = _____/10

Reading Informational Text Lesson 13

Text Features

Review the Standard (RI.4.7)

- **Interpret** information found in **charts** and **graphs**
- Explain how the information from a chart or graph **connects** to a text

Q: How do I **interpret** a **chart**, a **graph**, or other diagram?

A: A **chart, graph,** or diagram gives information in a visual way, using shapes, lines, and pictures instead of words. See if you can **interpret**, or figure out, what information is explained in the following samples.

Field Day Schedule

Event	Time	Place
High Jump	10:00 a.m.	Lonzak Field
Broad Jump	10:30 a.m.	Lonzak Field
Softball	10:00 a.m.	Martin Field
Races	11:00 a.m.	Lonzak Field
Soccer	1:00 p.m.	Martin Field
Double Dutch	1:30 p.m.	Lonzak Field

What Children Ate at the Picnic

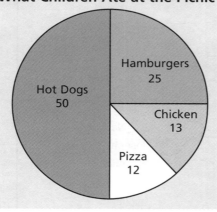

Hot Dogs 50
Hamburgers 25
Chicken 13
Pizza 12

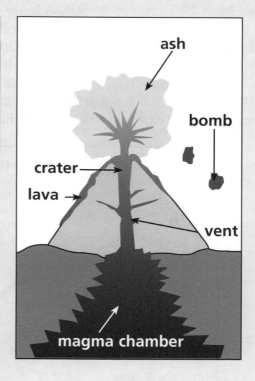

ash
bomb
crater
lava
vent
magma chamber

Q: How do I **connect** a chart or graph with the passage I'm reading?

A: Charts and graphs help you "see" what is being explained in the passage. Sometimes a chart will give you more facts or details about something you read. You should **connect** the information in the chart with what you read by asking questions: *What did I learn from the chart? How does the information in the chart fit with what I read in the passage?*

GO ON

Directions: Read the selection. Then answer the questions that follow.

Oregon Fever

1   Jobs were scarce in America in the early 1840s. Poor families in the Midwest wanted better lives. They began heading west to Oregon. They took horses and cows with them. They packed other possessions in covered wagons. Sometimes they took chickens in cages attached to their wagons.

2   The small wagons were narrow and about 14 feet long. Hoops over the wagon bed supported the cover, which was usually a thick, oiled cotton. The wagons rolled on huge iron-covered wheels. A team of four to six oxen pulled this heavy load.

3   The wagons carried food, tools, bedding, and a few clothes and pieces of furniture. Riding space was tight. One person sat on the driver's seat to guide the oxen. Babies rode in cradles. Other family members walked.

4   The 2000-mile trip to Oregon took four to six months. Wagon trains traveled the Oregon Trail for over 25 years. More than 400,000 people made the hard journey. Many people who started the trip did not survive.

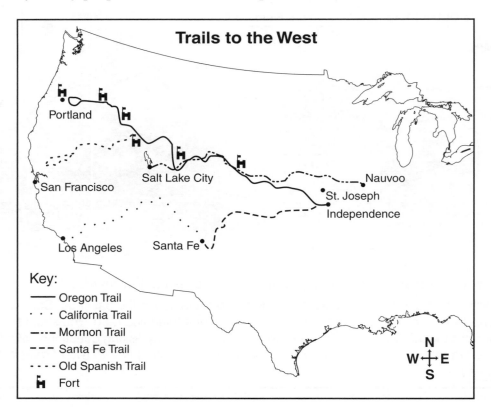

Trails to the West

Portland

San Francisco

Salt Lake City

Nauvoo

St. Joseph

Independence

Los Angeles

Santa Fe

Key:
— Oregon Trail
· · · California Trail
–·–· Mormon Trail
– – – Santa Fe Trail
· · · · Old Spanish Trail
Fort

N W E S

1   According to the map, the Oregon Trail started in—

   A Santa Fe.

   B Independence.

   C Salt Lake City.

   D Portland.

2   According to the map, how many different trails could a pioneer take to reach the West?

   A 3

   B 4

   C 5

   D 6

3   Which of the following information is found in BOTH the passage and the map?

   A Wagon trains traveled west to Oregon.

   B Some families took chickens and other animals with them.

   C Wagon trains traveled the Oregon Trail for over 25 years.

   D Many people who traveled to Oregon didn't survive.

4   Study the illustration of the wagon. Explain three facts about wagons from the text that the picture helps you understand. (3 points)

   _____

   _____

   _____

   _____

   _____

   _____

   _____

   _____

You must use the map to answer **Examples 1** and **2**. The title "Trails to the West" tells you what the map shows. The key tells you what the symbols on the map mean. The compass rose shows you the directions of north, south, east, and west on the map.

To answer **Example 1**, you must identify the Oregon Trail on the map. Look at the key to see what the symbol for the Oregon Trail is. Then, find this symbol—an unbroken line—on the map. The unbroken line starts in *Independence*, so **choice B** is correct.

Example 2 asks how many trails to the West there were, according to the map. The map's key lists 5 trails. **Choice C** is correct.

To answer **Example 3,** you must connect information from the map with information from the passage. Study the answer choices and then look at the map. You can eliminate choices B, C, and D because none of this information is found on the map. The correct answer is **choice A**.

Example 4 asks you to make a connection between the picture of the wagon and the facts about wagons on the Oregon Trail found in the passage. A good answer will give three specific facts from the text that can be seen in the picture.

Good: *The picture explains the following facts about wagons used on the Oregon Trail. First, the wagons had hoops that supported a cover. Second, the wagons rolled on huge iron-covered wheels. Third, the wagons were pulled by a team of four to six oxen.*

A poor answer will make an incorrect connection to the text or will not give three facts.

Poor: *The picture explains that the wagons carried food, tools, and bedding. There was a driver up front.*

◎ Try It On Your Own

Directions: Use the passage "Oregon Fever" and the graphs below to answer the following questions.

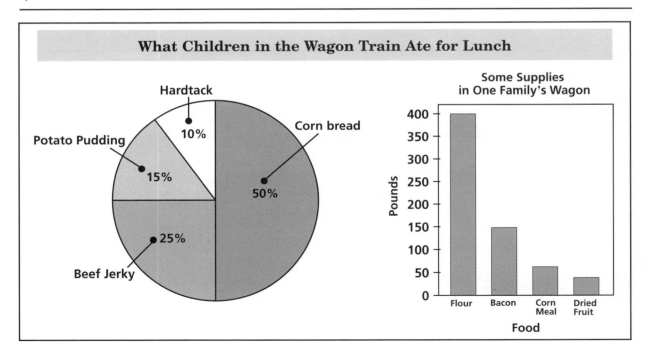

5 What did most children in the wagon train eat for lunch?

    A corn bread

    B hardtack

    C potato pudding

    D beef jerky

6 How many pounds of bacon did one family carry in their wagon?

    A 50 pounds

    B 75 pounds

    C 150 pounds

    D 400 pounds

7 How does the bar graph help you understand the passage? Which paragraphs does the bar graph give more information about? Be sure to use details from the passage in your answer. (3 points)

_____

_____

_____

_____

_____

_____

_____

Comparing and Contrasting Texts

Review the Standards (RI.4.6, RI.4.9)

- Compare and contrast a **firsthand** and a **secondhand** account of the same event or topic
- **Integrate** information from two texts on the same topic

Q: What is the difference between a **firsthand** and a **secondhand** account of an event?

A: A **firsthand** account is written by someone who actually experienced the events or things they are writing about. A **secondhand** account is written by someone who did not experience the events in person. A firsthand account will take you directly into the action and contain more personal emotions and thoughts about the event.

Q: How do I **integrate** information from two different texts?

A: To **integrate** means to bring together. Suppose you read two passages about Jesse Owens and the 1936 Olympics.

Passage 1: Jesse Owens was an African American runner who won four gold medals in the 1936 Olympics.

Passage 2: During the 1936 Olympics in Germany, Adolf Hitler believed that white Germans were better at running than black people.

Integrated: Jesse Owens showed Hitler that African Americans are excellent runners when he won four gold medals in the 1936 Olympics.

When you integrate information, you should think about how facts from different passages fit together.

 Try It

Directions: Read the following passages. Then answer the questions that follow.

The Battle of Trenton

In December 1776, America's hopes for victory in its war for independence seemed futile. George Washington and his troops had been chased out of New Jersey. The British were holed up for the winter in Trenton and other cities. Meanwhile, the American troops were at Valley Forge in Pennsylvania. They were cold, hungry, and ready to give up. The army was at its lowest number since the start of the war. And most of the men would have served their full time by January. Washington had to do something or the war would be over—and the British would win.

So Washington decided upon a bold move. He split his troops in half. Then he led 2,400 men by boat across the partially ice-filled Delaware River on Christmas Eve. They would surprise the enemy in Trenton. That city had been taken over by Hessians. They were soldiers hired from Germany to fight for Britain.

One member of the American forces was General Henry Knox. Shortly afterward, he described the battle of Trenton in a letter to his wife.

Delaware River, near Trenton
December 28, 1776

My Dear Lucy,

I must tell you about the battle that has changed the course of this war. Our poor, cold army was camped along the Delaware River. We knew the enemy forces were in Trenton, on the other side of the river. Bravely, General Washington decided to take the town by storm.

On Christmas Eve night, about 2,500 officers and soldiers crossed the river. Great chunks of ice were floating in the water. They made the trip nearly impossible. However, by 2:00 Christmas morning, we were all safely on the opposite shore. We landed about nine miles from Trenton.

The night was cold and stormy with terrible hail. Still, the men marched along silently, as ordered. We went in two groups. This was in case one group was discovered.

Just before dawn, both groups met at the edge of the city. The storm raged on. But at least it was now at our backs.

We marched a little farther. Then we came across a troop of Hessian guards. We immediately took them prisoner. Then we forced them along with us as we entered the town. There I saw war as I have never seen it before.

The Hessians were frightened and surprised. It was as if the last day of the world had arrived. They ran through the streets trying to form their armies. However, our cannons and guns put a stop to that. Next they tried to hide behind the houses, but we found them. At last they were driven out of town to an open area beyond. There they formed their armies once more.

However, we were ready for them. We had men posted along every roadway. The poor fellows soon saw that they were surrounded. The only way they could escape was to force their way through our troops. But they had lost their cannons to us. They had no choice but to give themselves up.

And so they did. Their chief officer, Colonel Rawle, turned everything over to General Washington. He gave away all their weapons, their flags, and about 1,200 men.

I am glad to tell you that there were few wounded or killed on either side. We marched the prisoners off. Then we took charge of their cannons and supplies. When all that was done, we went back to the spot where we had first landed.

Good fortune seems to have smiled down on us in this battle. If we take the proper steps now, we will surely win the war. How bravely our troops faced the enemy and forced them from the town. It must please all those who believe in the rights of mankind.

Your loving husband,
Henry Knox

1   Both the passage and the letter explain—

   A the actions of General Knox during the battle.

   B when the battle of Trenton happened.

   C how General Washington won the battle.

   D how many soldiers were killed.

2   How does the letter from Henry Knox add to the passage?

   A It tells an opposing point of view.

   B It gives an account of the battle from the British side.

   C It tells what his wife thought about the war.

   D It gives an account of the battle from someone who was there.

3   Who were the Hessians? Write a short paragraph integrating the information you learned about the Hessians from both the passage and the letter. (3 points)

   _____

   _____

   _____

   _____

   _____

   _____

   Example 1 asks you to **compare** the **firsthand** letter and the **secondhand** passage, or think about how they are alike. You can eliminate choice A because General Knox's actions are only described in the letter. The same is true of choices C and D. However, both passages clearly discuss when the battle of Trenton took place, although the letter goes into greater detail. The correct answer is **choice B**.

   Example 2 asks you to **contrast** the letter and the passage. You should think about how the focus of the passage and the letter is different. Since the letter gives an up close account of the events of the battle, the answer is **choice D**.

   To answer **Example 3**, you must **integrate** the information from both the passage and the letter. It may be helpful to return to the passage and underline information about the Hessians. The passage explains that the Hessians were hired soldiers from Germany. The letter explains how they were scared and surprised in battle. They didn't fight well and eventually surrendered. A good paragraph will bring together this information in a clear, well-written paragraph. Be sure to use complete sentences and correct punctuation.

   Good: *Hessians were soldiers hired from Germany to fight for Britain in the Revolutionary War. However, the Hessians were not very good soldiers because during the Battle of Trenton, they ran away scared. Washington and his army won the battle and eventually won the war.*

   A poor answer will only contain information from one text or will contain incorrect information.

   Poor: *Hessians were soldiers from Germany who came to fight against Washington.*

4   Read the following sentence from General Knox's letter.

I must tell you about the battle that has changed the course of this war.

Which of the following sentences from "The Battle of Trenton" supports Knox's opinion that the battle changed who was winning the war?

A *George Washington and his troops had been chased out of New Jersey.*

B *They were cold, hungry, and ready to give up.*

C *Washington had to do something or the war would be over—and the British would win.*

D *He [Washington] split his troops in half.*

5   Both the letter and the passage describe George Washington as—

A afraid.   **C** uncertain.

B brave.   **D** crazy.

6   Using information found in both passages, write a description of what happened the night Washington and his army crossed the Delaware River. (5 points)

_____

_____

_____

_____

_____

_____

_____

_____

Test-Taking Tips

1 Pay close attention to the headings on charts, maps, and graphs. They contain key information you need to understand the graphic.

2 Test questions may ask you to identify information found in both of the passages. Always return to the passages and make connections between them. Underline ideas that are the same. Pay attention to how one text goes into more detail or gives a different perspective than the other.

Go for it!

Unit Six Practice Test   Estimated time: 20 minutes

Directions: Read the following passages. Then answer the questions that follow.

VALLEY GAZETTE

June 12, 2009

Teenager Hit by Meteorite

Gerrit Blank, 14, was on his way to school in Essen, Germany, when he saw a "ball of light" heading straight toward him from the sky. A red-hot, pea-sized piece of rock then hit his hand, bounced off, and created a foot wide crater in the ground. The teenager came away with only a three-inch long scar on his hand.

"At first I just saw a large ball of light, and then I suddenly felt a pain in my hand. Then a split second after that there was an enormous bang like a crash of thunder. The noise that came after the flash of light was so loud that my ears were ringing for hours afterwards. When it hit me, it knocked me flying and then was still going fast enough to bury itself into the road," he explained.

Chemical tests on the rock have proved it had fallen from space. Ansgar Kortem, director of Germany's Walter Hohmann Observatory, said, "It's a real meteorite, therefore it is very valuable to collectors and scientists. Most don't actually make it to ground level because they evaporate in the atmosphere. Of those that do get through, about six out of every seven of them land in water," he added.

Meteorites striking humans are rare. There is only a one in a million chance of it happening. The only other known example of a human being surviving a meteor strike happened in Alabama, USA, in November 1954 when a grapefruit-sized fragment crashed through the roof of a house, bounced off furniture, and landed on a sleeping woman.

Chapter 10

Things That
Fall from the Sky

1 Have you ever seen a shooting star? These brief flashes of light in the night sky are not really stars at all. They're from chunks of rock that are falling from space toward Earth. As they enter Earth's atmosphere, they burn up. That's the light you see. Some of these chunks, however, manage to reach Earth before burning up. These are called *meteorites*. But where do they come from? And why do they fall to Earth? To find out, we'll need to explore the world of asteroids, meteors, and meteorites.

Asteroids

2 Asteroids are very small planets made of a dark, rocky material. They vary in size and shape. Larger ones have a round shape like the major planets. Smaller ones usually have irregular shapes. Most asteroids travel around the sun in our **solar system**. Their path is called the *Main Asteroid Belt*.

3 Scientists know about thousands of asteroids but are still discovering new ones. About 30,000 of the largest and brightest ones have been photographed. The largest known asteroid, Ceres, is about 600 miles wide. One of the smallest is less than a mile wide.

4 As asteroids move around the sun they sometimes crash into one another. The pieces that break off are called *meteoroids*. These pieces continue to move around the sun. Sometimes they move close to Earth's atmosphere. If they enter our atmosphere, gravity pulls them toward Earth.

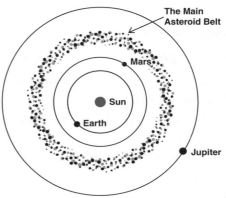

50

GO ON

Meteors

5   Meteors are streaks of light in the sky. They are caused by space dust or meteoroids entering Earth's atmosphere. As these pieces fall, air friction causes a trail of glowing gases. These burning gases are the bright streaks of light people sometimes see. Most meteoroids burn up completely before reaching Earth.

Meteorites

6   Meteorites are chunks of space rock that reach Earth's surface. Most are very small, and no one notices them. Some are found and identified later. Very few are actually seen landing on Earth. Scientists study meteorites to learn about the materials from which planets and moons were made.

7   Scientists think that some extremely large meteorites may have fallen to Earth in the past. People have discovered large holes called *craters* in several places around the world. One crater in Canada is 400 miles wide.

1   From the firsthand account of the boy who was struck by a meteorite, we learn that meteorites—

    A are very small planets.

    B make a loud noise when they enter the Earth's atmosphere.

    C usually land in water.

    D come from the Main Asteroid Belt.

2   The asteroid belt is located between—

    A Mars and Earth.

    B the Sun and Earth.

    C the Sun and Mars.

    D Mars and Jupiter.

3   Both passages explain—

    A how big the largest asteroid is.

    B how gravity pulls meteoroids toward Earth.

    C what a crater is.

    D that very few meteorites ever land on Earth.

4   Scientists would call the "ball of light" that Gerrit Blank saw in the sky—

    A an asteroid.

    B a meteor.

    C a planet.

    D a meteorite.

5 According to "Things That Fall from the Sky," shooting stars are—

   A asteroids.

   B meteors.

   C sun spots.

   D meteorites.

6 The diagram helps you understand all of the following EXCEPT—

   A where the Main Asteroid Belt is.

   B what planet is between Earth and the Main Asteroid Belt.

   C what the Main Asteriod Belt looks like.

   D how many miles the Main Asteroid Belt is away from the sun.

7 The focus of the newspaper article is to—

   A explain what a meteorite is.

   B persuade people to look for meteors.

   C explain the differences between asteroids, meteors, and meteorites.

   D describe what happened when a boy was hit by a meteorite.

8 What do these texts explain about meteorite craters? Write a short paragraph referring to specific facts. Be sure to integrate information from both passages. (3 points)

_____

_____

_____

_____

_____

_____

_____

_____

Points Earned/Total = _____ /10

Language
Lesson

Grammar

Review the Standards (L.4.1.a, L.4.1.d)
- Use **relative pronouns** and **relative adverbs**
- Order adjectives within sentences

Q: How do I use **relative pronouns** and **relative adverbs**?

A: Relative pronouns include *who, whose, whom, which,* and *that.*

Relative adverbs include *where, when,* and *why.*

These words connect adjective (describing) phrases to the noun or pronoun they modify.

Examples: My aunt, who lives in Spain, is studying art history.

The man, whose dog won the prize, has been training dogs for many years.

Saturday is the day when I relax.

The YMCA is the place where we go to play basketball.

Q: What order should I use for placing adjectives before a noun?

A: 1. *my/his/her* or *a/an/that* **2.** size (*big/small*) **3.** shape **4.** age (*old/new*) **5.** color **6.** material (*wooden/cement/brick*)

Examples:

My new blue cotton T-shirt is in the washing machine.

I want to buy that tall old wooden grandfather clock.

Try It

Directions: Choose the best answer for the following questions.

1   She told me _____ the party was.

A that

B whom

C where

D why

2 The person ____ won the prize was Olivia.

    A who

    B whom

    C where

    D which

3 I knew Dad was home when I saw _____ car was parked in the driveway.

    A his black big old

    B old black big his

    C his big old black

    D his big black old

    Example 1 asks you to choose the correct **relative pronoun** or **adverb** to fit in the sentence. Try reading the sentence with each answer choice. The only word that makes sense is *where*, **choice C**.

    Use the same strategy when answering **Example 2**. It is easy to eliminate choices C and D. Which is correct—choice A or B? Try reading just the phrase *who/whom won the prize. Whom won the prize* doesn't sound right. The correct answer is the subject *who*, **choice A**.

    Example 3 ask you to choose the answer that has the correct order of adjectives. Remember that words like *his* or *her* come first. Then size, age, and color. The correct answer is **choice C**.

◎ Try It On Your Own

Directions: The underlined portion of the following sentences is incorrect. Rewrite the sentences correctly on the lines.

4 I remember the day <u>where</u> the war began.

_____

_____

5 That is the reason <u>when</u> we don't eat too much candy.

_____

_____

6 I ran through the <u>green wide</u> fields of grass.

_____

_____

Usage

Review the Standards (L.4.1.b, L.4.1.c)
- Form and use the **progressive tense verbs**
- Use *can*, *may*, and *must* correctly

Q: How do I form **progressive tense verbs**?

A: Progressive tense verbs are formed with a helping verb (*am, was, will be*) and a verb that ends in *–ing*.

Action going on now: I am saving money to buy a new computer.

Action that happened at the same time as another action: I was saving money to buy a new computer when I lost my wallet.

Action that shows an ongoing or continuous action in the future: I will be saving money for many months.

Q: What is the difference between *can*, *may*, and *must*?

A: I can walk the dog. (You are able to walk the dog.)

I may walk the dog. (You might or might not walk the dog.)

I must walk the dog. (You are absolutely going to walk the dog.)

 Try It

Directions: Choose the correct answer for the following questions.

1   Right now I _____ a text to my friend.

   A am sending

   B was sending

   C will be sending

   D is sending

2   You _____ eat your dinner, or you won't get dessert.

   A can

   B may

   C must

   D might

3 Yesterday, I _____ when I tripped over a rock and stubbed my toe.

   A am running

   B were running

   C was running

   D will be running

For **Example 1**, you must think about which **progressive tense verb** fits in the sentence. Since the action is taking place right now, you need to use a present tense progressive. The correct choice is *am sending*, or **choice A**.

Example 2 tests your knowledge of how to use *can, may,* and *must*. It is understood from the sentence that if dinner is not eaten, you won't get dessert. The only answer choice that expresses that something has to happen is **choice C**, *must*.

Example 3 covers progressive tenses. The word *yesterday* used in the sentence is a clue that the action took place in the past. The subject *I* takes a singular verb so the correct answer is **choice C**.

◎ Try It On Your Own

4 Because I have taken lessons, I ___ play the piano.

   A can

   B might

   C must

   D may

5 Write a sentence using the verb phrase *must not go* correctly. (1 point)

   _____

   _____

6 Write a sentence using *was playing* correctly. (1 point)

   _____

   _____

Phrases and Sentences

Review the Standards (L.4.1.e, L.4.1.f)

- Form and use **prepositional phrases**
- Write **complete sentences**, recognizing and correcting inappropriate **fragments** and **run-ons**

Q: What is a **prepositional phrase**?

A: A **prepositional phrase** begins with a preposition and ends with a noun or pronoun.

Examples: *in the face, over the moon, around the house, after the game, of mine*

Q: How do I recognize a **complete sentence**?

A: A **complete sentence** expresses a complete thought. It has a subject and a verb.

Fragments and **run-ons** are not complete sentences.

Fragments	Fixed fragments
1. In the tree. 2. That my dad made. 3. Chasing the dog down the street.	1. The bird was in the tree. 2. The pie that my dad made was delicious. 3. The police officer was chasing the dog down the street.
Run-on sentences	**Fixed run-ons**
After school Jackie went to soccer practice Manny went to the library.	After school Jackie went to soccer practice, but Manny went to the library. (Add a comma and a conjunction.) OR After school Jackie went to soccer practice. Manny went to the library. (Use a period and a capital letter to create two sentences.)

Try It

Directions: Use the paragraph to answer questions 1–3.

> ¹The butterfly's different life stages. ²It starts out as an egg it turns into a pupa. ³The adult butterfly comes out of the pupa. ⁴Later the adult butterfly lays eggs. ⁵Then the stages start again for a new butterfly.

1 Which is a sentence fragment?

A sentence 1

B sentence 2

C sentence 3

D sentence 4

2 Which sentence is a run-on?

A sentence 1

B sentence 2

C sentence 3

D sentence 4

3 Which of the following parts of sentence 5 is a prepositional phrase?

A Then the stages

B stages start again

C start again for

D for a new butterfly

A sentence that does not have both a subject and a verb, or does not express a complete thought, is a **sentence fragment**. **Example 1** asks you to identify a sentence fragment within the passage. The first sentence in the paragraph, *The butterfly's different life stages*, is a sentence fragment because it doesn't have a verb. **Choice A is** correct.

Example 2 asks you to identify a **run-on sentence**. A run-on sentence is two or more complete sentences run together. Sentence 2 has two complete sentences all smashed together. The answer is **choice B**.

Example 3 tests your knowledge of **prepositional phrases**. Prepositional phrases begin with a preposition and end with a noun or pronoun. The correct answer is **choice D**.

4 Rewrite the paragraph above correcting the sentence fragment and run-on sentence. (5 points)

_____

_____

_____

_____

_____

_____

_____

Go for it!

Unit Seven Practice Test

Estimated time: 15 minutes

Directions: Use the following paragraph to answer questions 1–4.

¹Butterflies and moths are alike in some ways and different in other ways. ²They are both insects. ³They both have antennae and wings. ⁴Butterflies are usually brightly colored. ⁵Moths paler and not as pretty. ⁶Butterflies fly during the day moths fly at night.

1 Which of the following is a sentence fragment?

  A sentence 1
  B sentence 3
  C sentence 4
  D sentence 5

2 Correct the sentence fragment on the lines below.

_____

_____

3 Which of the following is a run-on?

  A sentence 2
  B sentence 3
  C sentence 5
  D sentence 6

4 Correct the run-on sentence below.

_____

_____

Directions: Read each question and then choose the correct answer.

5 In the sky is a _____ balloon.

  A yellow bright helium
  B bright yellow helium
  C helium bright yellow
  D yellow helium bright

GO ON

6 I am the one _____ you sit next to in class.

   A which

   B where

   C why

   D whom

Directions: Write the following sentences.

7 Use the verb phrase *can do* correctly in a sentence.

_____

_____

8 Write a sentence using a prepositional phrase. Underline the prepositional phrase.

_____

_____

9 Write a sentence using the verb *is running* correctly.

_____

_____

10 Write a sentence using an adjective clause that begins with the word *who*.

_____

_____

Points Earned/Total = _____/10

Language
Lesson
18

Capitalization and Spelling

Review the Standards (L.4.1.g, L.4.2.a, L.4.2.d)
- Use correct **capitalization**
- Spell grade-appropriate words correctly
- Correctly use frequently confused words

Q: What are the rules for **capitalization**?

A: **Capitalize** nouns and adjectives that name specific things.

> **Proper nouns:** Michelle Baker attends Jackson Middle School in Jackson, Mississippi.
>
> **Proper adjectives:** My Aunt Tina makes the best Mexican food.
>
> **Titles of books, TV shows, movies:** My favorite book is *The Hunger Games*, but Shaquille likes *Mockingjay* better.

Q: How can I identify spelling mistakes?

A: Use a variety of strategies to check for spelling mistakes. Be especially careful to check for homophones, or words that sound alike but are spelled differently.

> its/it's   to/too/two   there/their/they're   tow/toe

It is helpful to memorize words that are often misspelled, such as *finally, a lot, again, outside,* and *really.*

 Try It

Directions: Read each question and choose the best answer.

1   Complete the sentence below by choosing the word that is spelled correctly.

Yoko _____ the cave.

A exsplored
B explorred
C eksplored
D explored

2 Choose the sentence in which the underlined word is NOT spelled correctly.

  A Luke hit the <u>bawl</u>.

  B Here are <u>two</u> red roses.

  C My <u>bare</u> feet are cold.

  D Can he <u>heal</u> the sick dog?

3 Which sentence uses capitalization correctly?

  A My Parents and I went on a trip.

  B We visited my cousin's Farm.

  C My cousin hector has pigs and goats.

  D I helped Aunt Sasha gather eggs.

4 Which title correctly completes the sentence below?

Last week we read _____.

  A "the Silent forest of Fandia"

  B "The silent forest of fandia"

  C "The Silent Forest of Fandia"

  D "The silent Forest of fandia"

Example 1 asks you to choose the correct **spelling** of a word. **Choice D**, *explored*, is correct. The other choices show common spelling errors.

Example 2 tests your knowledge of **homophones**, or words that sound alike but are spelled differently and have different meanings. Each underlined word in Example 2 is a homophone: *bawl / ball*, *two / to / too*, *bare / bear*, and *heal / heel*. To answer the question, you must discover which homophone is used incorrectly. Choices B, C, and D all use the correct homophone for the context of the sentence. In choice A, the word *bawl* doesn't make sense because *bawl* means "to cry loudly." The homophone that does make sense in the sentence is *ball*. **Choice A** is correct.

To answer **Example 3**, you must be able to identify **proper nouns**. Proper nouns need to be capitalized because they refer to a specific person, place, or thing. In choice A, *parents* should not be capitalized because it is not a proper noun. For the same reason, *farm* should not be capitalized in choice B. The name *Hector* should be capitalized in choice C because it is a proper noun: Hector is a specific person, not just some boy or cousin. Choice D is written correctly because *Aunt Sasha* is a proper noun. **Choice D** is correct.

Example 4 asks you to find the **title** that has correct capitalization. All important words in a title are capitalized, including the first word. The word *of* should not be capitalized because it is a preposition and is not an important word. The correct answer is **choice C**.

5 Each sentence in the following paragraph contains one capitalization mistake. Rewrite the paragraph correcting all the capitalization mistakes. (5 points)

I am learning to speak chinese. Every afternoon I go to the Chinese Cultural Center next to our School. My instructor is dr. Anna Lee. She is from beijing, China. She even wrote a book called *the Chinese Way*.

_____

_____

_____

_____

_____

6 Each sentence in the following paragraph contains one spelling mistake. Rewrite the paragraph spelling all the words correctly. (5 points)

Fourth graders at are school used to get three recesses a day. That is alot of time to play. Now we only get two recesss a day. Kids our age need to get out side. It's not fare that we spend more time working than getting exercise.

_____

_____

_____

_____

_____

Language Lesson 19

Punctuation

Review the Standards (L.4.2.b, L.4.2.c, L.4.3.b)

- Use **commas** and **quotation marks** to mark direct speech and quotations
- Use a comma in a **compound sentence**

Q: How do I punctuate direct speech and quotations from a text?

A: Use a **comma** to set off *he said*, *she said*, or other speaker tags from what the person says. Put **quotation marks** around the speaker's exact words and direct quotations.

Examples:

Michael yelled, "What are you doing?"

"I'm cooking an egg in the microwave," Kia replied calmly.

"Don't you know," Michael said, "that it will explode?"

Michael found some advice from the microwave's manual: "Some products such as whole eggs may explode and should not be heated in this oven."

Q: How are commas used in **compound sentences**?

A: Commas are used before a conjunction (*and, but, for, nor, or, so, yet*) in **compound sentences**.

Mom said to pick up our rooms, or we would not be able to play outside.

I hate cold weather, but I love to go ice-skating.

www.photos.com

Study this chart to learn more about punctuation rules.

Punctuation Rules

☞ Every sentence needs a **punctuation mark**. Use a period, question mark, or exclamation mark, depending on the type of sentence.

> It is raining outside.
> How I hate rainy days!
> Will it be sunny tomorrow?

☞ Use a **period**—
- after an abbreviation.

  > Mr. Bates
  > Nov. 12

- after a person's initials.
  > Peter J. Morales

☞ Use an **apostrophe**—
- in contractions.

  > can't   I'm   he'd

- to show ownership.

  > the officer's badge

☞ Use **quotation marks** when telling the exact words someone says or said.

> Mom cried, "No muddy feet on the couch!"

☞ Use a **comma**—
- between a city and a state.

  > Fairbanks, Alaska

- in dates, between the day and year.

  > April 1, 2001

- in friendly letters, after the salutation and after the closing.
  > Dear Ashley,
  > Forever yours,

- to separate words in a series.

  > The playground has swings, slides, and seesaws.

- to set off certain words and phrases at the beginning of a sentence and in direct address.
  > Once upon a time,
  > Scamp, fetch the stick.

- before a quotation.

  > Ms. Biko said, "Quiet down."

GO ON

Try It

Directions: Read the following questions. Then choose the best answer.

1 Which sentence is punctuated correctly?

  A Martina shouted, "Watch out!"

  B Martina "shouted Watch out!"

  C Martina shouted, "Watch out!

  D Martina shouted "Watch out!"

2 Which sentence is punctuated correctly?

  A My favorite foods are tamales, and pizza.

  B I enjoy cooking but my sister never wants to help in the kitchen.

  C Carlotta came over last night, and we made tortillas from scratch.

  D I will bring you some tortillas or you can come to my house and eat them.

3 Which phrase correctly completes the sentence?

The hospital hired _____ last year.

  A Dr Beck

  B Doctor. Beck

  C Dr. Beck.

  D Dr. Beck

    Example 1 asks you to punctuate a **quotation** correctly. **Choice A** is correct. There should be a comma after *shouted* and quotation marks before *Watch* and after the exclamation mark. The other choices either leave out punctuation marks or put them in the wrong place.

    Example 2 tests your knowledge of **comma** use in **compound sentences**. Look at each sentence carefully. Choice A is not a compound sentence. It incorrectly uses a comma. Choice B is a compound sentence but is missing a comma before the conjunction *but*. Choice D is also a compound sentence and is missing a comma before *or*. Only **choice C** correctly uses a comma and a conjunction.

    To answer **Example 3**, you must understand how to punctuate abbreviations. The abbreviation for *Doctor*, *Dr.,* is always punctuated with a period. Choice A leaves out the period, and choices B and C put a period in the wrong place. **Choice D** is correct.

◎ Try It On Your Own

Directions: Read the following questions. Then choose the best answer.

4 Which sentence is punctuated correctly?

   A "Good morning," said the store manager.

   B They toured "the Food Mart" in Macon Georgia.

   C The manager showed the students how to order shelve and sell food.

   D "Does anybody have any questions." he asked.

5 Which sentence uses punctuation correctly?

   A The dedication in the book read To my dear friend and dog, Pickles.

   B I was told that we didn't have to read the book.

   C You must read the book or you won't understand the movie.

   D Mom asked, What time is the movie?

6 Which sentence uses punctuation correctly?

   A I love to go camping, but my sister hates it.

   B She would rather go to the mall, or stay in a hotel.

   C It is fun to sit around the campfire, and tell ghost stories.

   D My mother agrees with my sister and they usually get their way.

Test-Taking Tips

1 Check each sentence carefully, looking for errors in spelling. If a word doesn't look right to you, look at it again. It might be a misspelled word.

2 When you are working with homophones, be sure to read the sentence carefully. Look for clues that tell you which spelling is correct.

3 Capitalization can occur even in the middle of a sentence. Check every word in a sentence to look for possible errors.

4 If you see a group of words with more than one capital letter, pay close attention. The words might need all of the capital letters, but they might not. Look carefully at the group of words to decide.

5 When checking for correct punctuation, read each sentence to yourself to see if it sounds right. Often, when you pause while reading a sentence, there should be a punctuation mark.

Go for it!

Unit Eight Practice Test

Estimated time: 10 minutes

Directions: Read each question and choose the best answer.

1 Complete the sentence below by choosing the word that is spelled correctly.

The _____ closes at 10:00.

A resterant
B resteraunt
C restaraunt
D restaurant

2 Complete the sentence below by choosing the word that is spelled correctly.

It takes _____ to open this jar.

A strength
B strenth
C stregth
D strenghth

3 Choose the sentence in which the underlined word is NOT spelled correctly.

A Did you <u>break</u> the cup?
B The car sped <u>threw</u> the tunnel.
C What a handsome <u>knight</u> in armor!
D The rays of the <u>sun</u> are warm.

4 Which title correctly completes the sentence below?

Mrs. Brady's class saw the play _____.

A *Night Of Danger*
B *night of danger*
C *Night of Danger*
D *Night of danger*

5 Which phrase is capitalized correctly to complete the sentence below?

We saw many different kinds of dinosaur bones at the _____.

A Museum of Natural History
B Museum of natural history
C Museum Of Natural History
D museum of natural history

6 Which phrase is capitalized correctly to complete the sentence below?

The floors were made of _____.

A italian Marble

B Italian Marble

C italian marble

D Italian marble

7 Which sentence uses correct punctuation?

A Jenna asked "Has anyone seen the tennis rackets?"

B Jenna asked, "Has anyone seen the tennis rackets?

C Jenna asked, Has anyone seen the tennis rackets?

D Jenna asked, "Has anyone seen the tennis rackets?"

8 Which sentence uses correct punctuation?

A Mollys school was having a picnic at the park.

B Molly's mom dad and brother were all going.

C They took salad, sandwiches, and juice to the picnic.

D Molly's principal, Dr Dannen, gave a speech before everyone ate.

9 Which sentence uses correct punctuation and capitalization?

A The speaker said, "Kids and teens watch nearly 4 hours of TV a day."

B The speaker said, kids and teens watch nearly 4 hours of TV a day.

C The speaker said, "kids and teens watch nearly 4 hours of TV a day."

D The speaker said, kids and teens watch nearly 4 hours of TV a day.

10 Which sentence uses correct punctuation?

A Neither the dog, or the cat came when I called them.

B The dog usually comes running but, he didn't today.

C Romeo is a yellow lab, and Juliet is a calico kitten.

D My dog, and my cat fight all the time.

Points Earned/Total = _____/10

Language
Lesson
20

Word Meanings

Review the Standards (RI.4.4, L.4.4, L.4.4.a, L.4.6)
- Determine the meaning of words
- Use **context** as a **clue** to the meaning of a word or phrase
- Consult reference materials to find the **pronunciation** and determine **precise word meanings**

Q: How can **context clues** help me figure out a word's meaning?

A: Context clues are the other words in a sentence or sentences that can help you understand word meaning. Sometimes other words will give a definition or an example of the word.

Q: If I can't figure out a word's meaning from the **context**, what should I do?

A: If you still aren't certain of a word's meaning after checking the context clues, the next step is to look up the word in a dictionary or glossary. These reference materials will tell you more than one definition for the word and other information such as the part of speech and the **pronunciation** of the word. A dictionary entry will also help you figure out the **precise meaning** of a word that has multiple meanings.

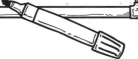

 Try It

Directions: Read the following passage. Then answer the questions that follow.

During the winter of 1777–1778, American soldiers experienced what was perhaps the worst time of the Revolutionary War. Congress decided to <u>train</u> the <u>troops</u>. George Washington chose Valley Forge as the training area because the enemy could not surprise them there. Washington set up training to teach farmers, storeowners, and schoolteachers how to fight a war.

The winter was harsh, and the young army had few supplies. Bringing new supplies to Valley Forge became impossible. The snow was too deep and the weather was too cold for wagons to travel there. Also, people who owned wagons did not want to risk wrecking them on the rutted roads. The soldiers had few clothes and shoes. Their feet and legs froze. They left bloody footprints in the deep snow. The army also had little to eat. Their meals were made up of a batter of flour and water fried into cakes. They drank water from the river. Many young men died that winter. <u>Bitter</u> cold and hunger killed some of them. Others died from diseases caused by unclean living <u>conditions</u>. Hospitals were so full of disease that anyone sent there was likely to die. Even if people were hurt or sick, there was little medicine for them.

However, during the following spring, wagons could travel to Valley Forge. General Nathanael Greene was made the officer in charge of sending in supplies. He knew how bad conditions were at Valley Forge. Fresh supplies arrived every day. A baker brought a group of 70 men to bake fresh bread every day. Soldiers were able to fish in the river, so they feasted on fresh fish.

Washington hired Baron von Steuben to teach the troops to fight. At first, he taught 100 men. Von Steuben spent the daylight hours of each day putting the men through <u>maneuvers</u>. They marched and practiced forming battle lines. When they had finished training, they each taught other groups. The main thing that von Steuben taught the soldiers was how to use their bayonets. As the troops began to learn fighting skills, the men became happier. They were proud of the new skills they were learning. As the newly trained troops moved out to fight battles, more men came in to be trained.

In June of 1778, the well-trained American army defeated the British in the battle of Monmouth. Everyone then knew that the farmers, storeowners, and schoolteachers who had spent such a terrible winter at Valley Forge were now a real army. The British now had an enemy to fear.

---

1 Read the dictionary entry for the word <u>train</u>.

> **train** (trān) *n.* **1.** the part of a gown that follows behind the person wearing it **2.** a line of railroad cars connected to each other *v.* **3.** to direct the way a plant grows **4.** to teach to be able to do something

Which definition BEST fits the meaning of <u>train</u> as used in the passage?

A definition 1
B definition 2
C definition 3
D definition 4

2 From the context, you understand that a *bayonet* must be—

A a weapon soldiers use to fight.
B a row of soldiers.
C a type of uniform.
D an officer in charge of soldiers.

3 As used in the passage, what does the word <u>maneuvers</u> mean?

A classes
B plans
C training exercises
D chores

GO ON

Example 1 asks you to choose the correct definition of a **multiple-meaning word** using a dictionary entry. You must choose the meaning that fits the way *train* is used in the passage. Since *train* is used as a verb in the passage, you can rule out definitions 1 and 2. And since the passage is not about plants, you know that definition 3 is also incorrect. That leaves definition 4, *To teach to be able to do something*. **Choice D** is correct.

Example 2 asks you to figure out what a word means from the **context clues**. The context explains that Baron von Steuben taught the troops to use their bayonets. The next sentence uses the phrase "fighting skills." We can determine from the context that a bayonet must be a weapon used to fight, or **choice A**.

Example 3 is a question about a **content** word. *Content words* are words that are used in a specific content area, or subject. Words used in math are math content words, and words used in social studies are social studies content words. *Maneuvers* is a military word that means *training exercises*, **choice C**. Often when you see content words, you may have to look in a dictionary to find which definition is correct for the content.

◎ Try It On Your Own

4   Reread the following sentence from the passage.

Others died from diseases caused by unclean living <u>conditions</u>.

Which definition BEST fits the meaning of <u>condition</u> as used in the passage?

A   an idea
B   the way something is
C   sickness
D   something needed from the environment

5   Read the dictionary entry for the word *bitter*.

> **bitter**   *adj.*   **1.** tasting bad   **2.** very determined   **3.** very great or intense   **4.** feeling unforgiving; full of regret

Which definition BEST fits the meaning of the word <u>bitter</u> in the passage?

A   definition 1
B   definition 2
C   definition 3
D   definition 4

6   Where else might you hear the word *troops* used in the same way as it is in this passage?

A   when reading a math book
B   when reading about World War I
C   when reading a fairy tale
D   when studying about animal habitats

Word Parts and Relationships

Review the Standards (L.4.4.b, L.4.5.c)

- Use **word parts** to determine word meaning
- Demonstrate understanding of words by relating them to their **antonyms** and to their related **synonyms**

Q: How can I use **word parts** to help me determine the meaning of a word?

A: Word parts include prefixes, roots, and suffixes. Knowing the meanings of common prefixes, roots, and suffixes will help you figure out new words. For example, *telegraph, photograph,* and *autograph* are all formed from the root *–graph,* which means "to write." It is also helpful to remember common prefixes and suffixes. Study these charts.

Prefix	Meaning	Example
un-	not, opposite of	unhappy, untie
re-	again	repaint
dis-	not	dislike
in-	not	indecisive
mis-	wrong	misfit
pre-	before	preheat
post-	after	postgame

Suffix	Meaning	Example
-less	without	careless
-ous *-ful*	filled with	marvelous, careful
-er, -or, *-ist*	one who does something	painter, sailor, artist

Q: What are **synonyms** and **antonyms**?

A: Synonyms are words that mean nearly the same thing (calm/peaceful). **Antonyms** are words that mean the opposite of each other (calm/crazy). Thinking about synonyms and antonyms of words will help you understand their meanings.

GO ON

Directions: Read the following passage. Then answer the questions that follow.

Trash or Treasure?

1 Olivia flopped onto the sofa with a sigh. "I'm bored," she said.

2 "You can help me unpack these boxes," Mom said. She <u>gestured</u> to a stack of dusty <u>cartons</u> beside the sofa. "These are filled with Grandma's collection of historical items. I'm helping her <u>reorganize</u> everything."

3 "Sounds really exciting," said Olivia, rolling her eyes.

4 "Who knows," said Mom, smiling. "Maybe you'll <u>discover</u> a long-lost treasure."

5 That got Olivia's attention. She opened the flaps of the box nearest her. A pile of black and white photographs spilled out. "Boring," she said.

6 Mom just smiled.

7 Olivia opened a smaller box. A puff of dust filled her nose, and she sneezed. Then her eyes grew round.

8 "Money!" she shrieked. "Look, Mom. A stack of paper money. But it's <u>unlike</u> any money I've seen before. Is it <u>real</u>?"

9 Mom came over to take a look. "Don't <u>mistake</u> these bills for play money," she said. "This is Confederate currency. During the Civil War, the Confederacy printed its own money. When the South lost the war, the Confederate money became <u>worthless</u>."

10 "Worthless?" said Olivia disappointedly.

11 "Worthless back then," said Mom. "Nowadays, Confederate currency is a <u>collector</u>'s item. You have a real treasure in your hands, Olivia."

1 Based on the meaning of the prefix *un-*, what does the word <u>unlike</u> mean?

   A not like

   B to like first

   C to like again

   D very similar

2 What is the prefix of the word <u>reorganize</u> in paragraph 2?

   A *org*

   B *organ*

   C *re*

   D *an*

3 A synonym for the word <u>cartons</u> from paragraph 2 is—

   A magazines.

   B rows.

   C boxes.

   D chairs.

4 An antonym for the word <u>real</u> is—

   A fake.

   B true.

   C money.

   D similar.

A **prefix** is a word part added to the beginning of a word to change its meaning. To answer **Example 1**, you need to know that the prefix *un-* means "not." When this prefix is added to the word *like*, the meaning becomes "not like." **Choice A** is correct.

Example 2 tests your ability to identify the prefix in a word. A prefix always comes at the beginning of a word, so you can rule out choices A, B, and D. In the word *reorganize*, the prefix is *re-*. **Choice C** is correct.

Example 3 asks you to find a **synonym**, or a word that means nearly the same as the word *cartons*. Cartons are containers or boxes. **Choice C** is the best answer.

To answer **Example 4**, you must identify an **antonym** for the word *real*. Of the answer choices, the only word that means the opposite of *real* is **choice A**, *fake*.

◎ Try It On Your Own

5 What is the root of the word <u>discover</u> in paragraph 4?

   A *over*

   B *cover*

   C *disc*

   D *dis*

GO ON

6 In paragraph 9, the root word of <u>mistake</u> is—

A *mis.*

B *stake.*

C *take.*

D *is.*

7 An antonym for the word <u>worthless</u> is—

A hateful.

B rare.

C valuable.

D trash.

8 A synonym for the word <u>gestured</u> from paragraph 2 is—

A picked up.

B pointed.

C looked at.

D carried.

9 Based upon its root, a <u>collector</u> is someone who—

A knows about money.

B throws things away.

C gathers and keeps similar things.

D steals money from banks.

Test-Taking Tips

1 A question may ask you to use a glossary or thesaurus to determine a word's meaning. A glossary is a list of words and their meanings, usually found at the end of a text. A thesaurus is a book that lists words and their synonyms.

2 Use every clue you can find to figure out the meaning of new words. When you don't recognize a root, suffix, or prefix, try looking for context clues. Sometimes clues are located near the unfamiliar word. Other times you must look in other paragraphs. Sometimes you'll understand the word only after you've read the entire passage.

3 When looking for synonyms, don't be fooled by choices that actually mean the opposite. Likewise when looking for antonyms, make sure you don't pick a synonym.

Go for it!

Unit Nine Practice Test

Estimated time: 15 minutes

Directions: Read the following passage. Then answer the questions that follow.

from Courage on the Oregon Trail

by Dorothy Francis

This passage is from a book about one family's journey west in the 1860s. Many families made this difficult, 2000-mile trip in hopes of finding a better life in Oregon. Twelve-year-old Luke and his ten-year-old sister, Ruthie, walk along the wagon and help whenever they can.

1 Pa said that *emigrants* were people who moved to a foreign country. Ma said that people who settled new lands were called *pioneers*.

2 Oregon had just become a state last month. So now it wasn't a foreign country. *Does that make us emigrants or pioneers?* Luke wondered.

3 Either way, they did a <u>heap</u> of walking. Oregon may be in the United States, but it was sure a long way from Missouri.

4 The Fletchers had packed everything they owned into <u>their</u> wagon. The blue and white cover would help keep things dry. Ruthie had helped Luke paint the wheels red. Ma said the colors showed they were proud to be Americans.

5 The wagon held their tent, tools, and food. Pa had added a <u>tiny</u> carpet, one chair, a box of china, and a mirror. Ma cried when she left behind their grandfather clock and the wooden bed.

6 Luke and Ruthie had each picked a few of their <u>special</u> things to take with them. The rest was left behind.

7 "Platte River up ahead!" the wagon master shouted.

8 "At last!" Luke called to Ruthie. "Something different."

9 They helped Pa <u>unhitch</u> the oxen. Each slowly began to <u>lead</u> a critter down the bank. Dirt and rock flew from under the oxen's feet.

10 Luke gasped when he fell. He slid down the bank on the seat of his pants. But he held tight to the rope. Digging in his heels, he slowed himself.

11 "Come and <u>guard</u> the oxen while they drink," Pa ordered Luke and Ruthie.

12 Ruthie stayed near the small oxen. Luke watched the two older ones. The oxen gulped and slurped. They drank as if they were filling <u>hollow</u> barrels.

13 Luke flopped on his stomach and drank too. He swished icy water around in his mouth until his teeth tingled. What a great feeling! Some folks said <u>cholera</u> came from drinking river water. But no one on their train had been sick yet.

1   In paragraph 3, a <u>heap</u> is a—

   A little bit.

   B great amount.

   C normal amount.

   D problem.

2   Read the following sentence from paragraph 4.

The Fletchers had packed everything they owned into <u>their</u> wagon.

Which of the following sentences also uses the word <u>their</u>?

   A ____ the best friends I've ever had.

   B Please put the box over ____.

   C They had to hold on to ____ hats.

   D ____ isn't time for that now.

3   Which word means the same as <u>tiny</u> in paragraph 5?

   A little

   B huge

   C old

   D useful

4   Which word means the opposite of <u>special</u> in paragraph 6?

   A exciting

   B expensive

   C small

   D ordinary

5   Read this sentence from paragraph 9.

They helped Pa <u>unhitch</u> the oxen.

After you <u>unhitch</u> oxen from a wagon, the oxen are—

   A not tied to the wagon.

   B tied to the wagon.

   C tied to the wagon again.

   D ready to be tied to the wagon.

6 Read this dictionary entry for the word <u>lead</u>.

> **lead** (lēd) *v.* **1.** to show the way by going in front of
> **2.** to be winning (led) *n.* **3.** a heavy metal **4.** a long, thin
> piece of graphite used in pencils

Which definition BEST fits the way <u>lead</u> is used in paragraph 9?

A definition 1
B definition 2
C definition 3
D definition 4

7 Which words help the reader know the meaning of <u>guard</u> in paragraph 11?

A *Digging in his heels, he slowed himself.*
B *. . . while they drink . . .*
C *. . . Pa ordered Luke and Ruthie.*
D *Luke watched the two older ones.*

8 Which word means the same as <u>hollow</u> in paragraph 12?

A empty   **C** old
B hard   **D** small

9 After reading the last two sentences in paragraph 13, the reader can guess that <u>cholera</u> is—

A good luck.
B something to eat.
C a disease.
D very cold.

10 Read the thesaurus entries.

> **tingle** (*v*) prickle, sting, tickle, itch
> **trail** (*n*) path, track, road, route
> **train** (*n*) file, line, procession

According to the thesaurus, another word for <u>trail</u> is—

A *file.*
B *route.*
C *sting.*
D *train.*

Points Earned/Total = _____/10

Mastery Test: Part 1   Estimated time: 30 minutes

Directions: Read the passage. Then answer the questions that follow.

My Best Shot

1 The referee blew the whistle. Shoes squeaked on the wood floor as the last quarter of the game began. So far in this game, I had tried to make my body do the best it could. I tried to jump up and rebound the ball. I tried to shove my long arms in front of opponents trying to score. And I tried to get my crazy giraffe legs to hustle down the court.

2 All in all, everything was working pretty well—except my aim. I just couldn't get the ball into the basket. No matter how hard I tried, it was one heartbreaking miss after another. Once again, it seemed certain I would have a scoreless game. Once again, the cheers would go to the girls who made the baskets.

3 This was one of our last basketball games of the season. We were fighting for our lives against the league's best team— the Wildcats. If we lost this game, there was no hope of advancing to the championship series.

4 We played hard. The Wildcats were quick, but so were we. They took risks, and so did we. It was a <u>close</u> game. Yet with seven seconds left, we were still losing by one point.

5 Then our luck began to change. The other team let the ball go out-of-bounds! The referee blew the whistle, and the ball was ours. One basket could win the game. Our coach called a time-out.

6 "Okay, Panthers," she said. "Here's our chance. I want to use our out-of-bounds play that we practiced. Let's make it work this time." She looked at me.

7 I panicked. We had practiced the play countless times and, in theory, it was a great play. But our fifteen-year-old minds and bodies rarely made it work. My teammates were supposed to block the other players while I ran toward the basket. When I was in good shooting position, they were to throw me the ball. Then I was supposed to make the shot. I was grateful for this chance. But my teammates almost never kept the other players out of the way, and even when they did, I almost never made the shot. Right now, a missed shot would surely ruin everything.

8 The buzzer sounded. Time-out was over. We got into our positions. The referee handed the ball to Jackie, who would throw the ball in from out-of-bounds. She took the ball, gave it a slap, and instantly threw it in to Tanya. If we wanted to win, we had just a few precious seconds to make this work. My legs took off.

9 What happened next was nothing like practice. My teammates were all over the other team. Not a single Wildcat could get anywhere near me! I found myself completely clear and ready for the ball.

10 "Over here!" I shouted. My heart pounded, and my palms were slippery. Someone hurled the ball at me. I remember thinking that if there was one time I really needed to hold on to a ball, it was now. So when that ball hit my hands, I held tight. Then as quickly as I could, I turned and dribbled toward the basket.

11   I stopped and looked up. All of a sudden the gym was quiet, and everyone in it was as still as statues. I had the eerie feeling they were all waiting for me to bring them back to life. With no time to think, I simply had to trust my body to know what to do. I aimed and gave the ball its final shove toward the basket.

12   I could feel all eyes follow its long journey. It arched high toward the ceiling, then started to make its way back down. After about a century, it hit the rim with a thud and started to circle around and around the edge. Finally, just as the buzzer sounded, it tumbled in.

13   The gym erupted with both cheers and groans. My teammates surrounded me, shouting with joy. There couldn't have been a better time for me to make my best shot ever.

---

1   When the narrator says the ball took "about a century" to reach the basket, she means—

    A it froze in the air and stayed there for a hundred years.

    B it seemed to take a really long time.

    C the ball went out-of-bounds.

    D while waiting for the ball, she took time to daydream.

2   Who is telling the story?

    A a third-person narrator

    B the referee

    C the coach

    D a first-person narrator

3   At the beginning of the story, the main character could be described as—

    A confident.

    B tired.

    C discouraged.

    D lazy.

4   Which sentence best expresses the theme of the story?

    A Always do your best and never give up trying.

    B You can always rely on your teammates.

    C Winning basketball games is fun.

    D It pays to follow all the rules.

GO ON

5 Describe what the main character thinks about her body at the beginning of the story. Be sure to use examples from the story to support your answer. Does the main character think differently about her ability at the end of the story? Explain. (3 points)

_____

_____

_____

_____

_____

_____

_____

_____

_____

Thief on Horseback

by Dorothy Francis

This passage is from Courage on the Oregon Trail, *a story about an American family's journey across the American western frontier in the 1860s. Many families traveled in covered wagons toward Oregon during that time. They hoped to find good land and a better life in the West. The Fletcher family includes twelve-year-old Luke and his younger sister, Ruthie.*

1   Luke heard the thumping of Ruthie's shoes. They were wearing thin, and the soles were flapping as she walked.

2   The Fletchers had walked beside their covered wagon for a month. Now they were deep into Nebraska. Fort Kearney lay two days behind them.

3   Ruthie yanked off her shoes. She threw them into the tall prairie grass.

4   "What are you going to do now?" Luke asked.

5   "Go barefoot," Ruthie said. "June is barefoot time."

6   "Jumpin' horned toad, Ruthie," Luke said. "It's a long way to Oregon. Fetch the shoes and tie 'em back on."

7   "You're not my boss," Ruthie said. "My feet hurt. I'm done with shoes." Ruthie's dark eyes flashed. Anger flushed her face clear up to her dark bangs.

8   Luke sighed. Ruthie looked a lot like Pa. But unlike Pa, she often acted silly. She needed a brother's advice. After all, he was two years older than she was. He knew so much more than she did. But Ruthie got mad as a wasp in a bottle if he mentioned that.

9   "Give me knife."

10   The deep voice startled them. They hadn't heard anybody approach. Ruthie ran to the other side of the wagon.

11   Luke looked up at the Native American riding a skinny horse. Green paint was smeared on his face. Black spiky hair bristled down the middle of his bald head. Bones and teeth circled his neck on a strip of leather.

12   The hair on Luke's nape stiffened. His heart was a pounding drum.

13   "Give me knife," the Native American repeated. He rode close and raised a club.

14   Luke could smell the sweat of the tired horse. He pulled the hunting knife from his belt and handed it to the man. Fear grabbed Luke's tongue. He held his breath.

15   The thief kicked his pony and cantered away. Luke breathed again.

---

6   Read this sentence from paragraph 8.

But Ruthie got mad as a wasp in a bottle if he mentioned that.

What is the meaning of this sentence?

A Ruthie got mad when she saw wasps.

B Ruthie flew around like a wasp if Luke mentioned he knew more.

C Ruthie got mad if she couldn't catch a wasp.

D Ruthie got very mad if Luke mentioned he knew more.

7   Summarize the passage. Be sure to include the main idea and any important events in the story. (3 points)

_____

_____

_____

_____

_____

_____

_____

_____

8   How is the point of view of this story different from the point of view used in "My Best Shot"?

A It is written in third person instead of first person.

B It is written in first person instead of third person.

C There is no narrator.

D One of the characters is telling the story.

GO ON

Directions: Continue reading about Luke and his family in a play version of the story.

from the play Courage on the Oregon Trail

ACT I, Scene 1

MA, PA, *and the wagon master,* JAKE, *enter.*

MA: Oh, Luke! (*She hugs him tightly for a long time.*)

JAKE: Are you hurt?

LUKE: N—no. But he took my knife—the knife my brother made. Mark carved my initials on the walnut handle.

JAKE: You're lucky you only lost a knife, boy! Peter Lee said Indians killed an emigrant last month. They don't always take kindly to us tramping through their lands. Now I guard Peter Lee's leather bag when he's out scouting.

RUTHIE: What's in it?

JAKE: Peter Lee doesn't say. And I don't pry. (JAKE *pats* LUKE'S *shoulder.*) Peter Lee knows Indian ways. He also knows the trails through this wild country. I listen to his advice.

PA: Peter Lee says many Indians are friendly. They often help repair wagons. Sometimes they show emigrants where to hunt.

JAKE: Yes. You did right, Luke. It's smart to be friendly with Indians.

MA: Yes, Luke. If your brother Mark were alive, he would have given up the knife too.

LUKE *closes his eyes and hangs his head. The lights fade.*

End of Scene 1.

9 Based upon the passage, we can infer that Peter Lee—

A is a Native American.
B has traveled the Oregon Trail many times.
C has never been to Oregon before.
D doesn't like Native Americans.

10 The last thing that happens in the scene is—

A Jake speaks to Luke.
B Ma speaks to Jake.
C Luke closes his eyes and hangs his head.
D the curtain goes down.

11 The next part of the play will be called—

A ACT II
B ACT I, Scene 2
C Part 2
D Chapter 2

Directions: Read the poem and answer the questions that follow.

From a Railway Carriage

by Robert Louis Stevenson

1   Faster than fairies, faster than witches,
   Bridges and houses, hedges and ditches;
   And charging along like troops in a battle,
   All through the meadows the horses and cattle:
5   All of the sights of the hill and the plain
   Fly as thick as driving rain;
   And ever again, in the wink of an eye,
   Painted stations whistle by.

   Here is a child who clambers and scrambles,
10   All by himself and gathering brambles;
   Here is a tramp who stands and gazes;
   And there is the green for stringing the daisies!
   Here is a cart run away in the road
   Lumping along with man and load;
15   And here is a mill and there is a river:
   Each a glimpse and gone for ever!

www.photos.com

12   You know this is a poem because—

   A it is shorter than prose.
   B it has rhyme and rhythm.
   C it is meant to be performed for an audience.
   D it is nonfiction.

13   Which line from the poem rhymes with line 8?

   A line 4
   B line 5
   C line 6
   D line 7

14   Which phrase from the poem includes a simile?

   A *charging along like troops in a battle*
   B *in the wink of an eye*
   C *all by himself and gathering brambles*
   D *lumping along with man*

15   In the second stanza of the poem the writer is describing—

   A what he sees as he rides a train.
   B the scenery around his house.
   C a picture of a train.
   D what he sees from the railroad station.

GO ON

16 The picture helps you understand—

    A what a railroad carriage is.

    B how fast railroad cars go.

    C the cart described in line 13.

    D what the mill in line 15 looks like.

Directions: Read the following passage. Then answer the questions that follow.

How the Bluebird and Coyote Got Their Colors

A Tsalagi Story

Many moons ago the bluebird used to be white. One day he was flying and came upon a lake and saw how blue and beautiful it was. He stopped and asked Grandfather, "Grandfather, can I be as blue as that lake?" So Grandfather gave him a song to sing. He told him what to do. Every morning for five mornings the bluebird would dive down into the lake singing the song taught to him by Grandfather, then come back up. The whole time he was doing this the coyote was watching him. On the fifth day, the bluebird dove into the lake, and when he came back out, he was as blue as he is today.

The coyote saw this and thought to himself, "Hmmmm . . . I'd like to be as blue as that bluebird." So he said to the bluebird, "Teach me your song." So every morning for the next five days, the coyote would take a bath and sing the song from Grandfather. And on the fifth day, the coyote came out and was just as blue as the bluebird. The coyote looked at himself in the reflection of the water and thought, "My, I'm the prettiest coyote there is. There is none prettier than me." So he strutted down the road, not unlike a peacock, looking around to make sure all the other animals could see him. He was so <u>intent</u> on having everyone know how colorful and beautiful he was that he paid no attention to where he was going. He ran into a tree, fell down into dirt, rolled around, and came up. That's why he's brown and dirty today.

17 From the context, the word <u>intent</u> means—

    A careful.

    B resourceful.

    C pretty.

    D focused.

18 In this story, Coyote could best be described as—

A imaginative.

B musical.

C hard-working.

D proud.

Directions: Read the following passage. Then answer the questions that follow.

Why Coyote Howls at the Moon

Many years ago, there was no moon. Night was very, very dark and it was difficult to see anything. The people complained because they were unable to visit each other or get any work done after the sun went down.

The people called together the creatures of the land and decided they would choose one of the animals to become the moon. Right away Fox raised his hand. So Fox climbed up into the sky.

As night came, Fox curled himself into a tight ball, laid down, and fluffed out his big, bushy tail in order to make himself into a perfect circle. Foxes' bright red fur reflected the sun's light very well. After several nights the people began to grumble. Fox was so bright, that they were unable to sleep! Poor Fox had tried so hard, but he was asked to come down from the sky.

The people decided that Crow would be a good moon because he was very dark and would not reflect the sun like Fox. As night came, Crow fanned out his beautiful tail feathers, tucked in his head, and spread his wings to make himself into a perfect circle. Crow's shiny black feathers glistened from the sun's light. After several nights, the people began to grumble. Crow's feathers would not reflect enough light for them to do any work after dark! People were running into trees, animals, and even each other. Poor Crow had tried so hard, but he too was asked to come down from the sky.

For a third time the people called together the creatures of the land. Coyote was always trying to help the people out and was always eager to try new things. So he offered to become the moon. He was neither too dark nor too light, and he could curl himself into a circle. He would be a perfect moon. So Coyote climbed up into the sky.

Coyote curled himself into a tight ball, tucked his nose under his tail, and fluffed out his fuzzy tail. He was indeed a perfect moon in every way. The people were able to visit each other after dark and work around the camp without running into each other.

But Coyote grew tired of always laying in the same position, doing the same job night after night. He began to look around and poke his nose into people's business.

"Hey," he would shout, so loudly everyone on Earth could hear him, "that man is stealing meat." He would look down over people's shoulders as they played games in the moonlight.

"Hey," he would shout, "that person there is cheating at the moccasin game."

The people came together for an important meeting.

"Coyote cannot be the moon!" someone yelled.

"He sticks his nose in everyone's business," yelled another.

"It's time for him to go!" grumbled several more.

So Coyote was forced by the people to come down from the sky. He was replaced by Rabbit. Rabbit was nearly the same color and able to make himself into a nice round circle. Rabbit did not have a nose for mischief.

Rabbit still is the moon even today. That is why on nights when the moon is round and close to full, you will see rabbit's nose and whiskers. That is also why, to this day, Coyote howls at the moon.

19 A synonym for the word <u>grumble</u> is—

   A complain.

   B whisper.

   C discuss.

   D thank.

20 The main character of "How the Bluebird and Coyote Got Their Colors" and "Why Coyote Howls at the Moon" is Coyote. What do you learn about Coyote's appearance, behavior, and personality from the stories? Be sure to use examples from the passages in your answer. (5 points)

_____

_____

_____

_____

_____

_____

_____

_____

Take a break. Then go on to Part 2.

Directions: Read the following passage. Then answer the questions that follow.

Christopher Columbus

(1451–1506)

Christopher Columbus was an **explorer** who sailed west across the Atlantic Ocean. He was searching for a sea route from Europe to Asia. In the 1400s, people in Europe were very interested in exploring Asia. They wanted to trade for gold, silk, **gems**, and **spices**. They also were interested in spreading the Christian religion. Few of them, however, wanted to make the long trip east to Asia across land. People began to search for a faster and easier sea route.

Explorers and traders first tried to reach Asia by sailing south around Africa. In 1492, Christopher Columbus tried sailing west across the Atlantic. This journey, however, did not take him to Asia. Instead, he reached a region that was later named the Americas. His journey was important because it introduced the people of Europe to the people of the Americas.

Early Life

Christopher Columbus was born in Genoa, Italy, in 1451. The exact date of his birth is not known. His father worked mainly as a **weaver**. The oldest of five children, Columbus went to school until the age of 14. He then began to work as a trader and **navigator**. He sailed on trading ships and later settled in Portugal. He met his wife, Felipa, there, and they had one son. During this time he also sailed to other places. He visited islands in the Atlantic Ocean and **trading posts** in western Africa.

The First Trip

In the late 1400s, scholars began to have new ideas about the shape of the Earth and the locations of different lands. Columbus listened to these new ideas. He became convinced that he could reach Asia by sailing west across the Atlantic Ocean. He began to plan a journey to Asia to set up a trading post. To find money for his journey, he talked to leaders in many countries. Most refused to offer him money. Finally, Queen Isabella of Spain agreed to help him.

Columbus set sail on August 2, 1492. He and his crew sailed west in three ships—the *Santa Maria*, the *Nina*, and the *Pinta*. The trip took much longer than expected. Many of the crew members became sick, and some began to doubt

GO ON

Columbus's ideas. But Columbus was determined to keep sailing. The ships finally reached land in mid-October. Columbus thought he had reached an island near Japan or China. But we now know that he actually reached an island in the Bahamas, south of Florida. He then explored the coasts of what we now call Cuba, the Dominican Republic, and Haiti.

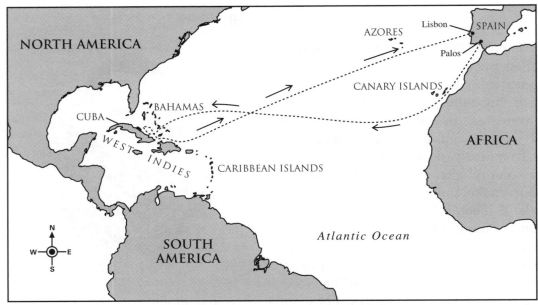

The route of Columbus's first trip

21 According to the passage, people wanted to explore Asia for all of the following reasons EXCEPT—

A to trade for gold, silk, and spices.

B to spread the Christian religion.

C to gain knowledge about the world.

D to make long trips across the world.

22

Problem: Columbus needed money for his trip.
Solution:

Which statement fits in the solution box above?

A Most leaders refused to offer him money.

B Columbus talked to leaders from many different countries.

C Queen Isabella of Spain agreed to help him.

D Columbus paid for the trip himself.

23 Why is the map included with the passage?

    A The map shows the route Columbus traveled.

    B The map shows lands explored by Spain.

    C The map shows how far Spain is from Africa.

    D The map shows where Columbus went on his last trip.

24 Shortly after Columbus left Spain, what did his ship pass?

    A the Caribbean Islands

    B the Canary Islands

    C the Azores

    D Cuba

Directions: Use the glossary to answer questions 25–27.

Glossary

explorer	person who travels to discover new places and learn about the land and people
gem	jewel
navigator	person who tells what route a ship should sail
spice	flavoring for food, such as cinnamon or pepper
trading post	a central spot where goods are exchanged
weaver	person who makes cloth from threads

25 Which glossary word can be used to describe salt?

    A explorer   **C** spice

    B gem   **D** weaver

26 The root of the word <u>explorer</u> is—

    A ex

    B plore

    C explore

    D er

27 Another word with the same root as the word <u>navigator</u> is—

    A naval

    B navigation

    C alligator

    D vigor

Directions: Read the following passage. Then answer the questions that follow.

Elections in the United States

1 The United States should change the way it elects the president and vice president. Every four years, we go through the same boring process. People who want to run for the offices go around the country asking people to vote for them. Most of these people can tell crowds why other candidates aren't qualified, but they can't explain why they, themselves, should be elected. They all say terrible things about one another to try to encourage people to vote one way or the other. This practice is called "mud-slinging" because candidates throw "mud" (in the form of mean words) at each other. The mud-slinging candidates hope that voters will view them as being a better choice than their opponents. But they're wrong! Voters just view them as politicians who can only say bad things about their opponents.

2 Then at party conventions, the two people who will run for president and the two who will run for vice president are chosen. Then the mud-slinging really begins. The candidates call each other bad names. Each talks about what a bad leader the other would make. The media compares their spouses, their children, and their pasts. The complaining and griping go on forever. Voters get really sick of hearing each candidate try to tear down the reputation of the other. Is this the kind of attitude our country is based on? Are we a country of arguers and name-callers?

3 I think we should hold elections like the British. The Prime Minister announces that elections will be held. Candidates are given two weeks to tell the people why they should be elected. When the two weeks are up, the people cast their votes. Then the whole process is over. True, British candidates also say horrible things about each other, but they have only two weeks to do it. Then the voters can have what they all really want—peace and quiet.

28 The structure of the passage is—

  A cause and effect.

  B comparison and contrast.

  C chronological, or order of events.

  D problem and solution.

29 The main idea of the passage is found in which of the following sentences?

  A *The United States should change the way it elects the president and vice president.*

  B *Voters get really sick of hearing each candidate try to tear down the reputation of the other.*

  C *Voters just view them as politicians who can only say bad things about their opponents.*

  D *Then the voters can have what they all really want—peace and quiet.*

30 The main reason why the writer doesn't like the way the United States elects its president is that the—

   A process takes too long.

   B candidates just say mean things about each other.

   C process is really boring.

   D media compares the candidates' families and backgrounds.

31 The main reason the writer thinks that British elections are better is because the—

   A candidates don't engage in mud-slinging.

   B Prime Minister announces the election.

   C process takes only two weeks.

   D British are nicer than Americans.

Directions: Read the selection. Then answer the questions that follow.

Oklahoma Times Reporter   **May 4, 2011**

Tornado Strikes!

1   Forecasters predicted a warm day with a slight chance of storms for yesterday morning. Noon forecasts called for a moderate chance of afternoon showers. By late afternoon, strong storms began to form above Oklahoma, in the heart of Tornado Alley. This is an area that stretches from Texas to Nebraska and then back down to Missouri. More tornadoes hit there than anywhere else in the country, with Oklahoma being the busiest place on the Alley.

2   Yesterday's storms were the result of warm air pushing north and encountering cold air still lingering from winter. At the same time, strong high-altitude winds were blowing above slower surface winds. This caused the winds to roll over each other, like wheels. Winds from a thunderstorm can tilt the "wheel," causing it to turn on its side. That is how a tornado is born. That's just what happened in the skies above Oklahoma yesterday—45 times. By late afternoon, twisters began sprouting up all over the state. And the biggest and most dangerous of all was heading straight for heavily populated areas of Oklahoma City.

3   Tornadoes are judged on a scale, from F-0 to F-5. Most tornadoes are F-1s and F-2s, but the one heading for Oklahoma City yesterday was an F-5, the largest and most dangerous. It was a mile wide and had winds of 318 miles per hour, the fastest ever recorded.

GO ON

4   The super-twister ripped through the suburb of Moore, then crossed I-35 into Oklahoma City and Midwest City. Entire neighborhoods disappeared—houses, cars, trees, everything. By morning, when all 45 storms had moved through the state, 43 people were dead, hundreds were injured, and thousands were homeless.

5   Recovery efforts began immediately. Rescue workers continue to sift through the remains of demolished houses, looking for survivors. University students are donating blood for the injured. Hundreds of volunteers are feeding the homeless. Donations of food and clothing are pouring in from all over the country. Once again people are showing that their will to survive is stronger than anything nature can throw at them.

32   Which is the best summary for this article?

A Oklahoma, in the center of Tornado Alley, was hit by 45 tornadoes on one May day in 2011. One of these, of the very destructive F-5 type, had the fastest winds ever recorded. It leveled whole neighborhoods around Oklahoma City.

B A tornado is a violent windstorm. Conditions have to be just right to form a tornado. Many tornadoes occur each year in Tornado Alley. They are classified from F-0 to F-5, depending on their strength. Tornadoes often hit Oklahoma.

C Tornadoes can be formed when warm air hits cold air and when strong, high winds blow over slower winds on the surface. The winds can roll like wheels and turn over on their sides. Oklahoma once had 45 tornadoes in one day. These storms can be very violent.

D It can be hard to predict tornadoes, but many of them occur in Tornado Alley. This is an area that stretches from Texas up to Nebraska and then into Missouri. After a tornado, students and other volunteers may help to clean up the damage.

33 The main idea of paragraph 5 is supported by—

A a description of the tornado's damage.

B examples of ways people are helping with recovery.

C a description of the tornado's path.

D reasons to take shelter during a tornado.

34 A forecaster is someone who—

A takes pictures of tornadoes.

B predicts the weather.

C writes newspaper articles about the weather.

D organizes recovery efforts for storm victims.

Directions: Read the selection. Then answer the questions that follow.

When the Tornado Hit

1 My name is Tory Brown. I'm 10 years old, and I lived through the worst tornado ever. It happened in a suburb of Oklahoma City, where I live.

2 The day started out pretty regular. I went to school, came home, and then went out to play. About 5:45, my mom called me in for dinner. Suddenly we heard the wail of tornado sirens. Because we live in the middle of Tornado Alley, our family has a plan for whenever the sirens go off. A few seconds later, Mom and I were in the bathtub, pulling a mattress over us for protection. About two minutes later the twisters hit.

3 Most people say a tornado sounds like a huge locomotive. I thought it sounded like a swarm of giant bees. As the roar grew louder, the bathtub started vibrating, and we could hear breaking glass. Then we felt something heavy hit the top of our mattress. About a minute later, the noise and vibrations stopped.

For a few seconds it was calm. Then we heard another roar that sounded as if things were being sucked up and carried away. It was the loudest sound ever. A minute later, the storm had passed.

4 Carefully, we lifted the mattress a few inches. We couldn't believe what we saw—or didn't see. The bathroom walls were gone. In fact, our entire house was gone. And so were most of the neighbors' houses. We were sitting in a bathtub in the middle of a field of <u>rubble</u>! With a little effort, we pushed the mattress off us. Turning around, we saw that the thing that had hit the mattress was a microwave oven from someone's kitchen.

5 People started appearing, crawling out from whatever they had hidden under during the storm. No one cried. We all just looked around at the piles of rubble that used to be our homes. It was too much for tears. I figured we would cry later, when the shock wore off.

35 Write a summary of the passage. (3 points)

_____

_____

_____

_____

_____

36 We can infer that Tory and her mother pulled a mattress over themselves because—

   A its thickness would protect them from heavy objects.

   B they were afraid they would be cold.

   C they didn't have enough time to get outside of the house.

   D the mattress would be a place for them to sleep later.

37 Why do you think Tory's family has a plan of action in case the sirens go off?

   A They live in Tornado Alley, where tornadoes are common.

   B They want to protect their ears from the loud sirens.

   C They want to protect their ears from the loud locomotive.

   D They are afraid of a swarm of giant bees.

Directions: Use "Tornado Strikes!" and "When the Tornado Hit" to answer the following questions.

38 BOTH of these selections—

   A explain what causes tornadoes.

   B give information about a severe tornado.

   C persuade people to avoid tornado situations.

   D present a problem and offer several solutions.

39 An important difference between these selections is that only one—

   A tells about a personal experience.

   B makes it clear how dangerous tornadoes can be.

   C describes how things looked afterward.

   D mentions Tornado Alley.

40 Use details from BOTH selections to retell the story of the tornado that hit Oklahoma City. Be sure you tell the story's events in the correct order. (5 points)

_____

_____

_____

_____

_____

_____

_____

_____

_____

_____

_____

_____

_____

_____

_____

_____

_____

Take a break. Then go on to Part 3.

41 Which sentence uses capitalization correctly?

   A My Uncle took me to see a movie yesterday.

   B The movie was called *My favorite Day*.

   C It was about a girl's memories of one Thanksgiving.

   D I really enjoyed going to the movies with uncle Jon.

42 Which sentence is punctuated correctly?

   A "Ling said I'll be glad to help."

   B Ling said, "I'll be glad to help.

   C Ling said, "I'll be glad to help."

   D Ling said, I'll be glad to help.

43 Which sentence uses capitalization correctly?

   A In spanish class, we sometimes watch movies.

   B Our teacher just showed us a Mexican Film.

   C I tell my friends that they should switch from french class.

   D My teacher is from a South American country.

44 Choose the sentence in which the underlined word is NOT spelled correctly.

   A We will stay at the <u>inn</u>.

   B Did Emma <u>dye</u> her hair red?

   C You are my <u>dear</u> friend.

   D <u>Nun</u> of the toys interest me.

45 Complete the sentence below by choosing the word that is spelled correctly.

Joni was _____ when her team lost.

   A disappointed

   B disapointed

   C dissappointed

   D dissapointed

46 The law says you _____ have a license to drive a car.

   A may

   B can

   C must

   D might

47 We don't know for sure yet, but we _____ go to Mexico over spring break.

   A may

   B can

   C should

   D will

48 Which of the following uses correct punctuation?

   A The author of the book writes, "Over 80 percent of homes in America have more than one TV set."

   B The author of the book writes Over 80 percent of homes in America have more than one TV set.

   C "The author of the book writes Over 80 percent of homes in America have more than one TV set."

   D The author of the book writes Over <u>80 percent of homes in America have more than one TV set.</u>

49 Tomorrow, I _____ a test in math.

   A am taking

   B was taking

   C have been taking

   D will be taking

50 Which of the following sentences has adjectives in the correct order?

   A My dog looks like a furry big monster.

   B However, she has friendly an attitude.

   C We built her a wooden huge doghouse.

   D She likes to lick you with her rough red tongue.

51 My mom is the woman ____ won the creative writing contest.

   A who

   B whom

   C where

   D why

GO ON

Directions: Use the paragraph to answer the following questions.

[1]Some of the planets that travel around our sun are known as "gas giants." [2]They are called *giants* because they are very large the term *gas* refers to what the planets consist of. [3]Mostly of gas, rather than rock. [4]The four gas giants are Jupiter, Saturn, Uranus, and Neptune.

52 Which of these is a sentence fragment?

　A sentence 1

　B sentence 2

　C sentence 3

　D sentence 4

53 Which of these is a run-on sentence?

　A sentence 1

　B sentence 2

　C sentence 3

　D sentence 4

54 On the lines below, rewrite the paragraph so that there are no sentence fragments or run-on sentences. Be sure to use correct capitalization and punctuation. (3 points)

_____

_____

_____

_____

_____

_____

_____

_____

Points Earned/Total = _____/70

Keeping Score

	Points Earned / Total Points	Percent Score
Tryout Test	/70	%
Unit One Practice Test Reading Literature: Key Ideas and Details	/8	%
Unit Two Practice Test Reading Literature: Craft and Structure	/12	%
Unit Three Practice Test Reading Literature: Integration of Knowledge and Ideas	/10	%
Unit Four Practice Test Reading Informational Text: Key Ideas and Details	/10	%
Unit Five Practice Test Reading Informational Text: Craft and Structure	/10	%
Unit Six Practice Test Reading Informational Text: Integration of Knowledge and Ideas	/10	%
Unit Seven Practice Test Language: Standard English	/10	%
Unit Eight Practice Test Language: Capitalization, Punctuation, and Spelling	/10	%
Unit Nine Practice Test Language: Vocabulary	/10	%
Mastery Test	/70	%

1. Fill in the number of points you earned in the Points Earned box.

2. Use the Finding Percent chart on page 156 to figure out your Percent Score. Then fill in the % box.

3. Compare your Percent Scores for the Tryout Test and the Mastery Test. See how much you've learned!

Finding Percent

⇨ Number of Points on Test

8

1	2	3	4	5	6	7	8
13%	25%	38%	50%	63%	75%	88%	100%

10

1	2	3	4	5	6	7	8	9	10
10%	20%	30%	40%	50%	60%	70%	80%	90%	100%

12

1	2	3	4	5	6	7	8	9	10	11	12
8%	17%	25%	33%	42%	50%	58%	67%	75%	83%	92%	100%

70

1	2	3	4	5	6	7	8	9	10	11	12	13	14	15	16	17
1%	3%	4%	6%	7%	9%	10%	11%	13%	14%	16%	17%	19%	20%	21%	23%	24%

18	19	20	21	22	23	24	25	26	27	28	29	30	31	32	33	34
26%	27%	29%	30%	31%	33%	34%	36%	37%	39%	40%	41%	43%	44%	46%	47%	49%

35	36	37	38	39	40	41	42	43	44	45	46	47	48	49	50	51
50%	51%	53%	54%	56%	57%	59%	60%	61%	63%	64%	66%	67%	69%	70%	71%	73%

52	53	54	55	56	57	58	59	60	61	62	63	64	65	66	67	68
74%	76%	77%	79%	80%	81%	83%	84%	86%	87%	89%	90%	91%	93%	94%	96%	97%

69	70
99%	100%

WRITING TEST
WORKSHOPS

Writing Test Workshops

To the Student

Why Do I Need This Book?

This book will help you practice taking writing tests. You will learn how to—

- read a writing prompt.
- get your ideas down on paper.
- write to tell a story.
- write to explain.
- write about an opinion.

How Will My Writing Be Scored?

Your writing test will be scored by test readers who use rubrics, or scoring guides. The rubric below lists six qualities of good writing. Read through each characteristic so you know how your writing will be graded.

Rubric					
Score: *1* is the lowest; *5* is the highest					
Ideas/Content—focuses on one main idea; the details add to the main idea	①	②	③	④	⑤
Organization—has a clear beginning, middle, and end; the order is easy to follow	①	②	③	④	⑤
Voice—communicates feelings and personality; the writing is unique	①	②	③	④	⑤
Word Choice—uses colorful, fresh words in the right places	①	②	③	④	⑤
Sentence Fluency—uses both long and short sentences that flow smoothly	①	②	③	④	⑤
Conventions—has few or no spelling, capitalization, and punctuation errors	①	②	③	④	⑤

How to Manage Your Time During an Essay Test

You may have 20 to 45 minutes to complete a writing test, so it's important to have a plan.

If you have 20 minutes,

◎ read the prompt, circle key ideas, brainstorm, and organize ideas. **(5 minutes)**

◎ write the essay. **(10 minutes)**

◎ revise, edit, and proofread. **(5 minutes)**

How to Read a Prompt

A *prompt* is the assignment for a writing test. The prompt gives you directions. It also tells you what to write about.

> ◎ **Step 1**
>
> Read through the entire prompt. Decide what the topic is.
>
> ◎ **Step 2**
>
> Read through the prompt a second time, underlining key words (*explain, compare, tell*) that will help you focus your writing.
>
> ◎ **Step 3**
>
> Look for key words or phrases you might use in your main idea statement.

Chen's Prompt

Here is a prompt for Chen's test. Look at the key words he underlined. They helped Chen understand exactly what he was supposed to do.

Prompt

A new law is being considered in your state. This law would require all bicyclists to wear helmets, elbow pads, and kneepads. Do you agree or disagree with this new law? Write a paper that expresses your opinion. Support your opinion with convincing reasons. Be sure to explain your reasons in detail.

From the prompt, Chen will have to write about his opinion on the new law. His paper must include reasons that he will explain in detail.

Try It On Your Own

Now it's your turn. Read the prompt below. Underline the key words or phrases that might be helpful to someone taking a writing test.

Prompt

You may or may not have traveled much in your lifetime. But you have probably seen pictures of places you haven't been or heard others describe them. If you could go anywhere in the world, where would you go? Provide reasons for your answer.

GO ON

Writing About an Opinion

Review the Standards (W.4.1.a–d, W.4.4, W.4.5, L.4.3.c)

- Write an **opinion** piece, supporting a **point of view** with **reasons**
- Include an **introduction** and a **conclusion**
- Support reasons with **facts** and **details**
- Use **linking words** and phrases
- Use formal English when writing

Some writing tests will ask you to write about an **opinion**. This type of writing is also called *persuasive writing*. When writing about an opinion, you must explain your **point of view** and then give **reasons** in support of your opinion. Your paper should have three parts: an **introduction**, a body, and a **conclusion**.

Introduction

- introduces the topic
- states your opinion (main idea) in one sentence:

  I think the city should keep the Metro Pool open.

Body

- includes one or more paragraphs
- gives reasons supporting your opinion
- includes **facts** and **details** to explain your reasons:

  Reason: *The pool gives kids something to do in the summer.*

  Facts/Details: *Every day in the summer 50 to 100 kids go to the pool to enjoy a good time. If the pool is not open, kids will have nothing to do. They might get into trouble.*

The best reasons—
- involve safety or health issues
- involve spending money
- affect the most people

Facts and details might include—
- personal stories
- opinions from experts
- examples

Conclusion

- restates your **opinion**
- ends with a strong thought:

  Everyone will suffer if Metro Pool closes. Kids will be bored and parents will be frustrated. Let's work together to keep our pool open.

Try It On Your Own

Directions: Practice writing your own opinion statement based upon the following question: *Should students be allowed to ride bicycles to school?* Write your opinion statement below.

_____

_____

_____

_____

_____

Now list three reasons that support your opinion.

1. _____

2. _____

3. _____

Then write a sentence or two to conclude your argument.

_____

_____

_____

_____

_____

_____

_____

_____

Mario's Paper

Below is a prompt Mario was given on a writing test. Help him by underlining the key words for him.

Prompt

Some residents in your city have complained to the city council about the number of pets some people have. These residents claim that the pets are noisy and dirty and can destroy property. The council is considering a law that would limit the number of pets allowed to two. Anyone having more than two pets would be fined and forced to get rid of the extra pets. What do you think of such a law? Write a paper that states your opinion. Provide support for your opinion.

Before writing his paper, Mario used a chart to help him organize his ideas.

Topic: a law that limits the number of pets people can have

Opinion Statement/Point of View: I am against the city council passing a law on the number of pets people can have.

Reasons
1. Pets are possessions.
2. People are responsible for the problems pets cause.
3. Pets make people happy.

Directions: Read Mario's paper. Then complete the tasks in the Looking at Mario's Paper box.

People and Their Pets

People have had pets for 1000 of years. Some people love their pets as much as they love their kids! Some people have pets because they don't have any kids. The city council should not pass a law that limits the number of pets people can have.

First of all, a pet is a possession. In America, people are allowed to have as many possessions as they can afford. People have more than two cars, more than two TVs, and more than two couches or beds. So they should be allowed to have more than two pets. As long as they take good care of their pets, they should be able to have more than two.

Also, people are responsible for the problems pets cause. Not pets. People should be find if they're pets got into trouble. That would make them control their pets more and it would allow them to keep their pets.

Pets make people happy, they make people feel loved and appreciated. If people are happier with more than two pets, they should be allowed to keep them.

In conclusion, a law limiting the number of pets people have is wrong. People who take care of their pets should be able to keep them, no matter how many they have. People are responsible for the problems pets cause, so people should be fined. Pets make people happy. Pets are great!

Looking at Mario's Paper

1. Underline Mario's opinion statement.

2. Put a star next to each of Mario's reasons.

3. Circle any lively verbs and exact nouns.

4. Cross out Mario's last sentence and write one that will provide a stronger ending.

5. Put a box around any linking words or phrases.

6. Correct mistakes in capitalization, punctuation, and grammar.

GO ON

Try It On Your Own

Directions: Now it's your turn to take a practice writing test. Follow the steps in order. If your teacher gives you a time limit, make a plan by filling in the amount of minutes you have to complete each step.

Time Allowed

_____ minutes

> **Step 1**—Choose the prompt you want to write about. Underline any key words. (_____ minutes)
>
> **Step 2**—Brainstorm for some ideas on another piece of paper. (_____ minutes)
>
> **Step 3**—Fill in the organizer with your ideas. (_____ minutes)

Prompt —————————————————————————

Your school has had problems with food fights, yelling, and rudeness in the cafeteria. In order to stop this behavior, the principal is considering making a rule that students are not allowed to talk during lunch. How do you feel about such a rule? Write a paper stating your opinion. Use examples, reasons, and facts to convince your readers to agree with you.

Prompt —————————————————————————

Your school district is considering a policy that would require all students to have a computer to use at school. Consider whether you agree with this policy or not. Then write a paper stating your opinion. Support your opinion with good reasons, facts, and details.

Topic: _____

Opinion Statement/Point of View: _____

_____

Reasons
1. _____   _____
2. _____   _____
3. _____   _____

Step 4—Using your organizer as a guide, write your paper on a separate piece of paper. (_____ minutes)

Step 5—Go back and revise your paper. Finally, proofread your paper for mistakes in capitalization, punctuation, and grammar. (_____ minutes)

How Did You Do?

Directions: Now evaluate your own writing (or ask a friend to evaluate your writing). Complete the following tasks.

Consider This

1. **Ideas/Content** Underline the opinion statement.
   - Number the reasons that support the position statement.

2. **Organization** Can you identify the introduction and conclusion? Write **I** and **C** next to them.
   - Put a box around linking words such as *first, next, second, finally,* and *also.*

3. **Voice** Does the writing communicate a positive attitude or does it seem angry or sound like a know-it-all?

4. **Word Choice** Circle any words that seem especially fresh or vivid. Cross out any words that are not exciting or precise.

5. **Sentence Fluency** Put a check next to any sentences that seem too choppy or too long.

6. **Conventions** Check for any errors in spelling, capitalization, and punctuation.

Use your answers from the **Consider This** chart to help you fill in this rubric.

Rubric Score: *1* is the lowest; *5* is the highest					
Ideas/Content—focuses on one main idea; the details add to the main idea	①	②	③	④	⑤
Organization—has a clear beginning, middle, and end; the order is easy to follow	①	②	③	④	⑤
Voice—communicates feelings and personality; the writing is unique	①	②	③	④	⑤
Word Choice—uses colorful, fresh words in the right places	①	②	③	④	⑤
Sentence Fluency—uses both long and short sentences that flow smoothly	①	②	③	④	⑤
Conventions—has few or no spelling, capitalization, and punctuation errors	①	②	③	④	⑤

One way I can improve my writing is by _____

_____

Informative
Writing
Tests

Writing to Inform or Explain

Review the Standards (W.4.2.a–e, W.4.4, W.4.5)

- Write **informative** texts with an **introduction** and **conclusion**
- Develop the main idea using **facts**, **definitions**, and **examples**
- Use precise language and **linking words**

Writing that informs (or explains) gives information on a subject. Examples include explaining how to make a paper airplane, describing how tornadoes form, or describing how the digestive system works. An **informative** paper has three parts:

Introduction

- gets the reader's attention
- presents the main idea statement

Main Idea:
Starting a rock collection is easy.

▶ Grab Attention

- **Surprise your reader.** "One little brown bat can eat 600 mosquitoes in an hour!"

- **Entertain your reader.** Tell a story: "The first time I saw a bat, I screamed and hid in back of my big brother. I was sure it was going to land in my hair."

- **Challenge your reader.** Ask a question: "Are you one of the people who thinks bats are blind?"

Body

- includes one or more paragraphs
- uses good **linking words** between ideas (*first, next, then, later, in the same way*)
- supports the main idea by giving details, **examples**, **facts**, **definitions**, or quotations:

First, find a container to store and organize your rocks.

Next, find a good Web site or book that explains different types of rocks.

Now you are ready to search for rocks in your neighborhood or parks.

Conclusion

- sums up the paper
- contains a strong concluding thought:

Get yourself a good rock book, a sturdy box, and a few rocks. Before you know it, you'll be an official rock collector.

Try It On Your Own

Directions: The following is information from an informative paper on the topic "Why *Behind the Times* is my favorite TV series." Put a check mark next to the sentence that doesn't stick to the topic.

_____ The family in *Behind the Times* reminds me of my own family.

_____ I learn a lot about history because the stories take place in the past.

_____ *Behind the Times* episodes are very different from episodes in other series.

_____ I'm the only one in my family who likes *Behind the Times*.

_____ *Behind the Times* shows that people in the past were a lot like people today.

Gina's Paper

Below is a prompt Gina was given on a writing test. Help her out by underlining the key words for her.

Prompt

Everyone likes stories about genies who give wishes. Imagine that a genie offered you a wish for something you've always wanted: a pet, a bicycle, a computer. What would you wish for? Write a paper explaining what your wish would be. Give reasons for your wish.

Before writing her paper, Gina used an idea web to help her organize her ideas.

Words used in informative writing prompts
- compare/contrast
- define
- explain
- summarize
- tell

enter contests

teach him tricks

learn to ride

A horse

take care of him

give friends rides

Directions: Read Gina's paper. Then complete the tasks in the Looking at Gina's Paper box.

My Biggest Wish

Some people dream about visiting faraway places. Others dream about doing great deeds. I dream about horses. If I could have any wish, I would wish for a horse. If I had a horse, I could learn to ride like my cousin Samantha, I could even enter riding contests and maybe win a Blue Ribbon. I would hang my ribbons all over my room, if my mom would let me. She doesn't like it when I put holes in the walls. Not even thumbtack holes. If I had my own horse, I could take my friends for rides. We could trot threw the park and wave at all the kids. Sometimes we'd stop and let them pet him. If I had a horse, I would spend a lot of time brushing him. And making him beautiful. I would braid his mane. I would tie brightly colored ribbons in it. I would also teach my horse tricks like how to count, and how to walk backward. I would give him a treat everyday. He would always be happy to see me. I would love my horse, and he would love me. I would rather have a horse than anything in the world. People say that dogs are our best friends. Maybe that's true, but I'll take a horse any day!

Looking at Gina's Paper

1. Put an **M** next to Gina's main idea.

2. Does the essay have a clear beginning, middle, and end? Yes ____ No ____

3. Put a **P** where Gina should begin a new paragraph.

4. Cross out any sentences that don't fit with the main idea.

5. Circle any lively verbs or exact nouns.

6. Underline each sentence that begins with "I would." Rewrite two of these sentences using different subjects and verbs.

7. Mark and correct any errors in capitalization, punctuation, and spelling.

Try It On Your Own

Directions: Now it's your turn to take a practice writing test. Follow the steps in order. If your teacher gives you a time limit, make a plan by filling in the amount of minutes you have to complete each step.

Time Allowed

_____ minutes

> **Step 1**—Choose the prompt you want to write about and then follow the steps for reading a prompt. (_____ minutes)
>
> **Step 2**—Brainstorm for some ideas on another piece of paper. (_____ minutes)
>
> **Step 3**—Fill in the organizer with your ideas. (_____ minutes)

Prompt _____

Imagine you are trying to teach a younger child how to ride a bike. Explain the equipment he or she needs and the steps that should be taken to ride a bike.

Prompt _____

Do you have a dream about what you would like to do when you are older? Explain what it is and what you will need to do to accomplish your dream.

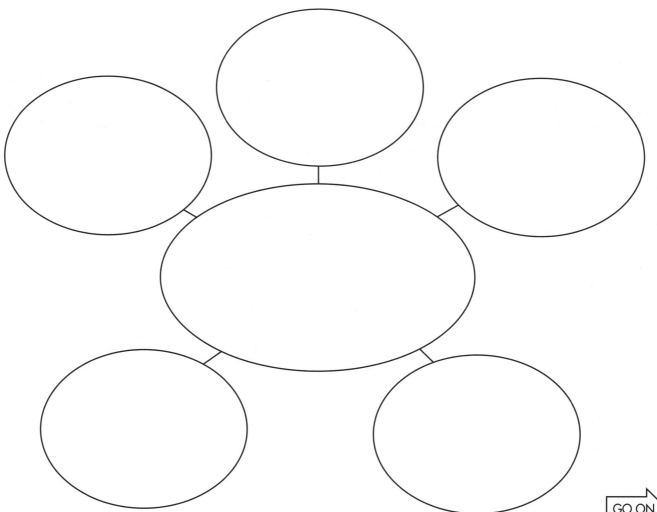

GO ON →

Step 4—Using your idea web as a guide, write your essay on a separate piece of paper. (_____ minutes)

Step 5—Go back and revise your paper. Finally, proofread your paper for mistakes in capitalization, punctuation, and grammar. (_____ minutes)

How Did You Do?

Directions: Now evaluate your own writing (or ask a friend to evaluate your paper). Complete the following tasks.

Consider This

1. **Ideas/Content** Underline the main idea statement.
   - Number the supporting details.

2. **Organization** Can you identify the introduction and conclusion? Write **I** and **C** next to them.
   - Put a box around linking words such as *first, next, second, finally,* and *also.*

3. **Voice** Put a **V** next to any part of the story where the writer's voice doesn't fit or seems strange.

4. **Word Choice** Circle any words that seem especially fresh or vivid. Cross out any words that are boring or not precise.

5. **Sentence Fluency** Put a check next to any sentences that seem too choppy or too long.

6. **Conventions** Check for any errors in spelling, capitalization, and punctuation.

Use your answers from the **Consider This** chart to help you fill in this rubric.

Rubric Score: *1* is the lowest; *5* is the highest					
Ideas/Content—focuses on one main idea; the details add to the main idea	①	②	③	④	⑤
Organization—has a clear beginning, middle, and end; the order is easy to follow	①	②	③	④	⑤
Voice—communicates feelings and personality; the writing is unique	①	②	③	④	⑤
Word Choice—uses colorful, fresh words in the right places	①	②	③	④	⑤
Sentence Fluency—uses both long and short sentences that flow smoothly	①	②	③	④	⑤
Conventions—has few or no spelling, capitalization, and punctuation errors	①	②	③	④	⑤

One way I can improve my writing is by _____

_____

Narrative Writing Tests

Writing to Tell a Story

Review the Standards (W.4.3.a–e, W.4.4, W.4.5, L.4.3.a)

- Write **narratives** about real or imagined experiences
- Explain a **situation**, **characters**, and **events**
- Use **dialogue** and **description**
- Choose words and phrases to convey ideas precisely
- Provide a **conclusion**

When you tell a story, you are narrating, or telling about **events**. That's why telling a story is called **narrative** writing. The events you are describing may have really happened to you or they may be made up. A narrative has the following parts:

Beginning

- introduces **characters** and a **situation** (a problem or conflict)
- describes the setting (when and where the story takes place)
- may include a main idea statement, for example:

  The day I forgot my best friend's birthday was one of the worst days of my life.

Middle

- contains the main events of your story that build by developing the problem or conflict
- uses time order words—*next, then, later, when, after*—to show event order (chronological order)
- Uses **dialogue** and **description**

Description—precise, lively words

"The sky turned gray as I pedaled my bike toward my house."

"What's **dialogue**?" Joey asked.

"It's talking between characters," Mia replied.

Joey said with a laugh, "Oh, like what we're doing right now!"

Ending

- provides a **conclusion** by explaining how the problem or conflict ends
- may tell what the characters learned:

  Once David got home, he promised himself that he'd never go exploring alone again.

- or may tell how the events changed you:

  I learned that I must look at my calendar in order to notice important dates.

GO ON

Try It On Your Own

Directions: Read the paragraph below. The events of the story are in order, but they could use come connecting words. From the list, put the letter of the best connecting phrase in the blank.

_____ my dad took my mom out to eat so we could get everything ready. _____ we decorated the living room and brought out the cake. _____ we heard them pulling in the driveway, so we lit the candles. _____ we turned the lights out and hid behind the furniture. _____ we turned on the lights and yelled, "Surprise!"

> **A.** We had just finished when
>
> **B.** Early in the evening,
>
> **C.** When they walked in the door,
>
> **D.** While they were gone,
>
> **E.** Then, as quickly as we could,

TyRay's Story

Below is a prompt TyRay was given on a writing test. Help him out by underlining the key words for him.

Prompt

Funny things happen to everyone. Tell the story of a really funny thing that happened to you or someone you know. What led up to the event? Who was involved? Why do you remember that particular event?

Before writing his paper, TyRay used a story map to help him organize his ideas.

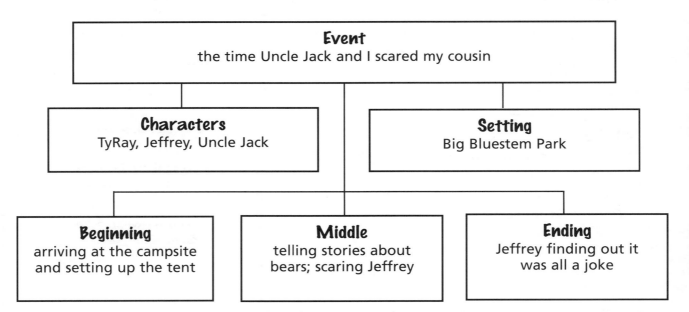

© Perfection Learning® No reproduction permitted.

Directions: Read Jeffery's paper. Then complete the tasks in the Looking at TyRay's Paper box on page 174.

Scaring Jeffrey

I'll never forget the time my uncle and I scared my cousin Jeffrey. Last summer, Uncle Jack took Jeffrey and me camping. Uncle Jack loves to play tricks on people. He was a football player in college. He has twinkly eyes and a booming laugh. My cousin Jeffrey is a year older than I am. Jeffrey is a show-off. He always acts like he's so brave. So I'm always trying to scare him, but it never works.

Big Bluestem Park is mostly woods. The campsites are in the middle of the trees. In the daytime, the tall trees are like a big, green ceiling above. But at night the park is kind of scary. The trees creak and moan, and owls and other creatures make all kinds of weird noises. The park was really crowded that weekend.

After supper, I asked Uncle Jack if he would help me scare Jeffrey. He said he would, so we made a plan. We sat around the campfire, and Uncle Jack told us stories about bears attacking people in the park. I could see Jeffrey was nervous because he kept looking around, watching for bears in the trees. After that, we

went into our tent and Uncle Jack went into his.

Jeffrey asked me, "Do you think there are really bears in this park?"

I tried not to smile. I said, "I don't think Uncle Jack would lie to us, do you?"

Just then we heard a snuffling and snorting outside our tent. Then something bumped into the side of it. "It's a bear!" I yelled.

Jeffrey started screaming, "Uncle Jack! Uncle Jack! There's a bear! Help!" He looked like he was about to cry.

Just then Uncle Jack stuck his head in our tent and said, "You called?"

I burst out laughing. Jeffrey looked confused for a minute, and then he started laughing too. Uncle Jack just rolled his eyes before tackling both of us to the ground. None of us will ever forget the time I scared Jeffrey.

Looking at TyRay's Paper

1. Put an **M** next to TyRay's main idea.

2. Does the story have a clear beginning, middle, and end? Yes ___ No ____

3. Does the story describe the characters and the setting? Yes ___ No ____

4. Underline linking words and phrases that connect the events.

5. Cross out any parts of the story that do not tie into the main idea.

6. Put a star next to examples of good dialogue and description.

Try It On Your Own

Directions: Now it's your turn to take a practice writing test. Follow the steps in order. If your teacher gives you a time limit, make a plan by filling in the amount of minutes you have to complete each step.

_____
minutes

Step 1—Choose the prompt you want to write about and then follow the steps for reading a prompt. (_____ minutes)

Step 2—Brainstorm for some ideas on another piece of paper. (_____ minutes)

Step 3—Fill in the organizer with your ideas. (_____ minutes)

Prompt ——————————————

Imagine you could be a superhero for a day. Decide what kind of powers you would have and what your name would be. Then tell the story of a good deed you performed as a superhero.

Prompt ——————————————

Write about a time when you conquered a fear. Was anyone with you? What was happening around you? What were you thinking of at the time? How do you feel about the experience now?

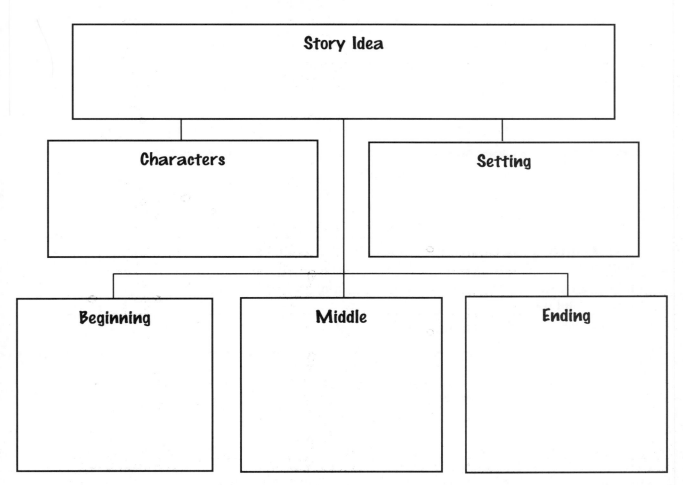

Story Idea

Characters

Setting

Beginning

Middle

Ending

GO ON

Step 4—Using your story map as a guide, write your story on a separate piece of paper. (_____ minutes)

Step 5—Go back and revise your paper. Finally, proofread for mistakes in capitalization, punctuation, and grammar. (_____ minutes)

How Did You Do?

Directions: Now evaluate your own writing (or ask a friend to evaluate your story).

Consider This

1. **Ideas/Content** Underline the sentence that contains the main problem or conflict in the story.
   - Put a check by any events that stray away from the main problem.
   - Put a smiley face next to good description or dialogue.

2. **Organization** Identify the beginning, middle, and ending of the story by writing **B, M,** and **E** next to where you find them in the story.
   - Put a box around linking words such as *later, next, then,* and *after.*

3. **Voice** Put a **V** next to any part of the story where the writer's voice doesn't fit or seems strange.

4. **Word Choice** Circle any words that seem especially fresh or vivid.
   - Cross out any words that are boring or not precise.

5. **Sentence Fluency** Put a check next to any sentences that seem too choppy or too long.

6. **Conventions** Check for any errors in spelling, capitalization, and punctuation.

Use your answers from the **Consider This** chart to help you fill in this rubric.

Rubric Score: *1* is the lowest; *5* is the highest					
Ideas/Content—focuses on one main idea; the details add to the main idea	①	②	③	④	⑤
Organization—has a clear beginning, middle, and end; the order is easy to follow	①	②	③	④	⑤
Voice—communicates feelings and personality; the writing is unique	①	②	③	④	⑤
Word Choice—uses colorful, fresh words in the right places	①	②	③	④	⑤
Sentence Fluency—uses both long and short sentences that flow smoothly	①	②	③	④	⑤
Conventions—has few or no spelling, capitalization, and punctuation errors	①	②	③	④	⑤

One way I can improve my writing is by _____

_____